100 INTERACTIVE ACTIVITIES

for Mental Health and Substance Abuse Recovery

14 TOPICS INCLUDE:

ASSERTION

COGNITIVE CHANGES

COPING

ANGER MANAGEMENT

INSPIRATION

SELF-REFLECTION

MENTAL HEALTH & SOBRIETY

STRESS MANAGEMENT

PROBLEM SOLVING

SELF-HELP

SELF-ESTEEM

RECOVERY

SELF-DEVELOPMENT

RELATIONSHIPS

D1478021

by Carol A. Butler, MS Ed, RN, C
Illustrator Amy Leutenberg Brodsky, LISW

WELLNESS
REPRODUCTIONS
& PUBLISHING, LLC
A Guidance Channel Company

ACKNOWLEDGMENTS

This book is dedicated to my husband
Richard R. Butler
the love of my life.
His wisdom, love, tireless advice and assistance made this book possible.

My deepest gratitude to

Ruth MacVittie, my mother, for nudges toward education, career and writing.

Marion MacVittie, my aunt, for steadfastly sustaining me.

Miss Dorothy Croll, my English teacher, for instilling literary appreciation and skill.

Carmela Potter, for endless revisions and faith in the outcome.

Estelle Leutenberg, Kathy Korb-Khalsa, illustrator Amy Leutenberg Brodsky, graphic designer Joan Allison, Lucy Ritzic and all Wellness Reproductions and Publishing, Inc. staff, for their guidance, expertise and commitment to excellence for professionals and clients.

Reviewers, for the time, effort and suggestions which greatly improved this book.

Clients, for their ideas, enthusiasm, perseverance in overcoming obstacles and for teaching me more than the greatest group could teach them!

ABOUT THE AUTHOR

Carol A. Butler has a Bachelor of Science Degree in Education, Master of Science in Education and School Counseling, a Certificate in Alcohol and Drug Studies, and is a Board Certified Psychiatric and Mental Health Registered Nurse. She is a member of the American Psychiatric Nurses Association and a member of the Alliance for Psychosocial Nursing.

Ms. Butler taught children and adults in public schools, has worked as counselor, grant writer, evaluator and placement specialist in vocational rehabilitation and as an Employee Assistance Professional. She has also developed programs and led groups for children, adolescents and adults who are recovering from mental, physical and substance abuse disorders in acute psychiatric hospitals and outpatient programs.

FOREWORD

Years ago as a substitute teacher, I needed a 'bag of tricks' to, at a moment's notice, engage potentially rowdy students. Spelling Charades evolved: it was interactive, fun, adaptable to any grade level, and only required words on slips of paper, students' imaginations and their willingness to 'ham it up'. An educator had advised me, "If you have to stand on your head to get their attention, do it". I quickly realized, getting them to 'stand on their heads', (figuratively), was more effective!

Years later, on a nineteen-bed adolescent psychiatric unit, the shift started at three o'clock in the afternoon. At four o'clock on weekends, facilitating a group was required. A 'bag of tricks' was again essential. Emotion Charades evolved. Other activities, with universal application were developed, addressing Maslow's Hierarchy of Needs and Defense Mechanisms, emphasizing peer interaction, downplaying authority and making it fun to learn.

Partial Hospital adult clients posed a new challenge. They were not a 'captive audience'. They had to awaken early, procure transportation and spend five to six hours a day in groups. Some were 'program-wise' and 'grouped-out' after months or years in 'the system'. Lectures and literature became 'old'. Competition among Partial Hospital Programs forced development of a variety of relevant, interesting and unique activities.

Today, compliance with insurance, government and accrediting agencies requires individualized treatment and accountability. Activities must meet each client's specific needs for survival skill acquisition and document personalized learning. Necessity for the provided level of care and progress toward recovery must be proven. Activities herein invite participants to apply dynamic principles to current crises.

Concurrent mental illness and substance abuse are common. Some traditional recovery programs lose some mentally ill clients who perceive needed confrontation as harsh criticism. A 'kinder, gentler' approach engages them. Integrating mental health and substance abuse recovery makes sense: concepts of disease, treatment, heredity, environment, attitude, actions, chemistry, catharsis, comradeship, coping, self- knowledge and spirituality apply to both.

Group leaders and participants, I applaud you for your daily struggles and conquests. Hopefully this book will help.

Carol A. Butler

Carol A. Butler, MS. Ed., RN, C

INTRODUCTION

"Give a man a fish and you feed him for a day. Teach a man to fish and you feed him for a lifetime."

This Chinese proverb applies to psychoeducational group leaders who adapt dynamic ideas to a lifetime of topics, and to group members who 'fish': think, feel, read, write, draw, dramatize, debate, play games, coach and counsel each other about Anger Management, Assertion, Cognitive Changes, Coping, Esteem, Insight, Inspiration, Mental Health, Problem Solving, Relationships, Self-Development, Self Help, Sobriety, and Stress Management. Facilitators and participants develop self-sufficient survival skills.

Children, adolescents and adults in psychiatric hospitals, community mental health and substance abuse recovery programs, schools, correctional institutions, boys and girls clubs and/or scouts, places of worship addressing emotional and addiction issues, vocational rehabilitation and other settings will benefit. Facilitators include social workers, counselors, educators, occupational therapists, nurses, psychiatric technicians, jail or prison staff, spiritual leaders and other paraprofessionals and professionals.

Authority figures talking at people turn them off. Facilitators or 'prime movers' perk them up by promoting peer interaction. Anxiety among group leaders abates when group members are in the spotlight. Participants flourish in a respectful, non-judgmental climate.

One hundred activities plus numerous variations meet challenges to get people to group, versus home or bed; keep them awake and alert despite apathy and drowsiness; move members literally from onlookers' chairs to 'spotlight seats'; move them figuratively from unhealthy to constructive thoughts, feelings and actions.

'Thrills and chills' replace 'fight or flight' among facilitators and participants as "what we have to learn to do, we learn by doing"*, through exciting, enlightening and enjoyable activities.

* Aristotle, Greek Philosopher

HOW TO USE THIS BOOK

Please read introductory information including 'HOW TO USE FACILITATOR INFORMATION SHEETS', 'THESE GROUPS ARE...', and 'TECHNIQUES TO BRING LEARNING TO LIFE AND LIFE TO LEARNING'. They provide valuable insights, tips, benefits and drawbacks of specific activities and pitfalls to avoid.

Peruse the TABLE OF CONTENTS for timely topics and flip through pages, noting LEGENDS on top right corners of FACILITATOR'S INFORMATION SHEETS, which indicate ages and ability levels.

Plan about fifty minutes per activity, but always take materials for a related topic in case they whiz through! Example: talkative participants will take fifty minutes discussing emotions portrayed in EMOTION CHARADES; quieter folks will need a second activity, such as PICTURE GAME, wherein they draw ways to handle the feelings.

If many staff members use this book, decide who addresses each topic to ensure no one 'steals the thunder' by doing today what a colleague plans for tomorrow. Each group leader can photocopy his/her favorites and keep them in a three-ring binder.

Intersperse interactive with introspective assignments (worksheets, reading, journaling, drawing). Let participants' energy level and time of day guide you. Usually mid-morning is best for reading, writing and discussing; early morning and after lunch are sluggish times: games and controversial debates sustain alertness.

Develop your own activities. Games like 'BINGO', 'TIC-TAC-TOE', 'CROSSWORD CLUES' and others are adaptable. Change the questions to incorporate the day's 'hot topics', such as peer pressure, safe sex and suicide prevention.

Incorporate skills developed during group into your charting. Specify participants' words and actions, illustrating their progress toward goals due to your therapeutic interventions.

Use disclosures, issues and behaviors occurring during group as a springboard for private discussion or counseling. Example: A teenaged boy laughed about serious issues, mocked peers and used profanity during group, yet disclosed guilt and low self-esteem in private. When asked about the discrepancy, (privately), he acknowledged nervousness and embarrassment around the girls. During the next group, he was more genuine. Example: many clients were shunning the more severely disabled peers, refusing to sit with them at lunch. An activity evolved, addressing scapegoats, illustrating that unhappy people with poor esteem often look for targets to trample.

Be yourself. Avoid rigid adherence to the formats provided, 'Go with your gut'! Adapt, add and delete suggestions to meet your people's needs and your personal style. Use whatever works!

HOW TO USE FACILITATOR'S INFORMATION SHEETS

Legend (explained on each topic overview page) indicates the appropriate ages, level of dfficulty and number of pages in each activity.

AGE	DIFFICULTY	PAGES

PURPOSE

PURPOSE states what participants will say and do during group; specifies cognitive and behavioral goals.

MATERIALS

MATERIALS are commonly available office or household items; 'board' implies blackboard, grease board or flipchart with portable easel; if no 'board' is available, a large piece of paper, taped to the wall suffices. 'Marker' implies chalk or dry-erase magic marker. Some activities have accompanying pages; some do not. Accompanying pages provide game boards, questions, lists, worksheets and reference information for facilitator and/or participants, Answer keys provide required responses but some activities have no right or wrong answers because their purpose is to stimulate thought, discussion, and self-expression in a non-judgemental environment. 'CUT-UP' pages are questions, directions, terms, words or phrases to be cut on the dotted lines and placed in 'container for CUT-UPS' such as envelope, small box, tray, bowl or cup. 'CUT-UPS' can be used 'as is' or affixed to index cards or photocopied onto heavier card stock for greater durability. Save them in labeled envelopes, plastic sleeves or plastic sealed bags. Play money 'CUT-UP' pages (SKILLS BILLS) are provided.

ATTENTION GRABBER

ATTENTION GRABBER whets appetite for learning, using props and participant volunteers. They incorporate visual aids, role-plays, writing or drawing on board while peers guess the topic or concept. They require brief coaching before group. Volunteers and facilitators are instructed to *elicit* – or draw out answers from participants. Giving hints and asking leading questions heightens interest; telling the answer destroys the suspense! *Brainstorming* implies people blurting out all possibilities without evaluating their feasibility or worth.

ACTIVITY

ACTIVITY describes the preliminary discussion and directions for games, role-plays, board work, art, written work, tasks for individuals, dyads (pairs), or teams. These are thought provoking, skill-building activities wherein they 'learn by doing'. The *process* is paramount! Applaud efforts to think, say, do and interact. 'Spotlight Seat(s)' refers to chair(s) at front of room, facing peers, occupied by a 'contestant' and/or 'host', peer leader or person(s) who are sharing answers, drawings, or other work.

FOLLOW-UP

FOLLOW-UP personalizes and summarizes the activity.

VARIATION

VARIATION describes alternative methods and/or topics depending on ages, ability levels and temperaments. Example: changing seats or standing under signs engages people exhibiting apathy or lethargy. Hyperactive children or adolescents acting 'antsy' might become overactive with this much movement, or it could appropriately channel their energy.

THESE GROUPS ARE...

- **Psychoeducation combined with psychotherapy:** Skills acquired augment group therapy. Discussion and disclosure are encouraged. Individual therapy with an audience is discouraged. On-lookers lose interest and drudging up past horrors is counterproductive. Concentrate on coping with current challenges.

- **Interactive versus lectures:** Participants aren't gobbling information with gusto to regurgitate on an exam! Many have poor concentration and short attention spans. Brevity, activity and relevance to immediate needs heighten interest. 'Variety is the spice of life' and learning! Great games become commonplace if overdone. Art, writing, drama and discussion incorporate multiple teaching methods.

- **Exploration of values versus courts of law:** Create a climate for self-acceptance or change, depending on individual needs. Positive peer pressure is more powerful than your authoritative admonishments. Avoid condoning or condemning drugs, dangers and unprotected sex, by asking questions. Giving them 'food for thought' beats 'ramming it down their throats'. You need not be judge, juror, or have the last word.

- **Spiritual growth opportunities:** Neither preach nor delve into doctrines. Life or death may hinge on belief in a Higher Power. Encourage introspection and tolerance for divergent beliefs. Poetry and 'words of wisdom' spark spirituality without specific ideology.

- **Interpersonal skill builders versus social events:** Discourage eating, drinking, and trivial conversation. Fifty-minute activities prohibit wasting time. Direct tangential talkers to stick to the topic. Breaks between groups are for food, beverages, bathroom and socializing.

- **Expression Enhancers:** De-emphasize spelling, grammar, penmanship, artistic and dramatic proficiency. Brainstorming and spontaneity flourish with instructions to "Let it all hang out!" or "Convey your thoughts and feelings whatever way works".

- **Contests where everyone wins:** Prizes promote excitement but don't use them for every game. Knowledge and skills are the most valuable rewards.

- **Flexible:** If you start with one topic or activity and clearly their interest and needs relate to another, do switch midstream. 'Go with the flow', provided it's productive.

- **Lessons that lessen stage fright! (yours and theirs):** Your 'butterflies' disappear when participants are the major players. Keeping them in the limelight enhances their learning, while lowering your self-consciousness. If you're uncomfortable with a topic, read reference material. 'Go with your gut'. If you can't picture something working for you or them, select an alternative. When you're well acquainted with group members and confident in your skills, be more daring!

- **"This Is Your Life" for the participants:** Be cautious about self-disclosure. They think their situation is unique and pitfalls and consequences you experienced "won't happen to me". If they ask personal questions, remind them, "I'm here for you; I want to talk about you". Refer them to support groups for 'people who have been there'. Encourage peers to answer their questions.

- **Nurturing, not parental:** Think, speak and treat in an adult to adult manner versus parent to child. Remember the self-fulfilling prophecy: they'll measure up or down to your expectations.

- **Professional and supportive versus stodgy, chummy or enabling:** This is not 'HELPLESSVILLE' and you are not their caretaker. Generate warmth without favors or familiarity. Don't foster learned helplessness. Elicit peer partnership, self-direction and self-actualization.

- **More than meets the eye:** If, despite your efforts, participants appear apathetic or antagonistic, remember: "Chance is always powerful. Let your hook be always cast; in the pool where you least expect it, there will be a fish" (Ovid, Roman Poet).

TIPS TO BRING LEARNING TO LIFE
AND LIFE TO LEARNING

1. **Literal to Figurative** – Tangible items displayed by 'volunteers' illustrate abstract ideas and spark interest. A few examples:

   Dump wastebasket on floor (to demonstrate what negative thoughts do to our mind)

   Distribute buttons (for "Don't let them push your buttons")

   Pass around tangled string (to demonstrate distorted thinking)

   Pass around a lemon and drink lemonade (to illustrate positive outcomes from adversity)

   Use a toy eye inside a toy brain; people guess what's inside (to demonstrate the mind's eye)

   Pass around a TV remote control and discuss on, off and channel changes (to illustrate thought stopping or substitution)

   Put masking paper on shoe sole (to demonstrate being 'stuck' in the past)

   Wear a mask (to illustrate how we hide our true feelings)

   Show coffee grounds in a filter (to demonstrate cognitive distortion of focusing on negatives)

2. **Games** – Apathetic people perk-up for points or prizes. Individuals win at *Bingo, Picture Game, Charades, Hangman* and others. Teams play *Crossword Clues, Tic-Tac-Toe, Ace the Quiz, To Tell the Truth, Who Wants to be a Pillionaire, Twenty-one,* and others. These offer excitement and eventually everyone wins. Repeat winners select someone who hasn't yet won to take the next turn. Person in the 'spotlight seat' may collaborate with teammates. No one is solely responsible for the team's win or loss. Points are lost for peer 'put-downs'. Try to evenly distribute high and low achievers between teams.

   The 'Game Show Host' may be the high achiever (who would overshadow everyone if competing) or a reticent person who'll 'bloom' in the limelight. A low achiever with adequate reading skills is elevated in this role. An angry or defiant person may 'rise to the occasion' and gain attention for positive behavior. The person with poor cognitive ability becomes highly important as scorekeeper and prize provider. Taking turns as 'Host' is advisable. Games have drawbacks. People are preoccupied with points and have low tolerance for discussion, except for debate among teammates regarding answers. Don't try to elaborate or lecture. Move it along. Intolerance for less capable members may rear its ugly head. Set ground rules ahead of time. No put-downs. Give everyone a fair chance to think and speak for himself/herself. Everyone can ask for and receive peer help. If all are stumped, ask leading questions or give hints but avoid giving an answer. People learn by arriving at their own conclusions.

3. **Role Plays** – Pantomime, playing parts in parables or portraying, then correcting cognitive distortions, mimicking defense mechanisms or other behaviors generate learning among actors and promote audience participation by discussing the performance's message. 'Coaches' in conflict resolution scenarios remind antagonists to take each step.

4. **Practice** – 'Practice makes perfect' as they make assertive statements, correct cognitive distortions, physically move to 'Yes' or 'No' signs, defend beliefs, debate and complete assignments.

5. **Board Work** – Peer interest heightens when 'one of their own' writes on the board. People pay attention knowing they'll have to 'go up there.' The physical movement generates interest. People claim their stage of recovery or their current need on Maslow's hierarchy with photos or initials. They lead peers in brainstorming negative then positive thoughts, feelings and actions or depict 'the big picture' or ways to be calm in chaos. Those in their seats remain 'on their toes' assisting peer at board or awaiting their turn at leadership.

6. **Questions and Answers** – Traditionally the teacher asks and students answer. Simulated talk shows, panel discussions, debates and speeches involve participants in asking and answering. They must think, define and assertively express their own values and face challengers. Incorporate 'hot topics', issues pertinent to their problems or their 'pet peeves.' Involve participants in developing questions openly or anonymously.

7. **Art** – De-emphasize artistic ability. Emphasize getting thoughts and feelings onto paper using scribbles, stick figures, symbols, colors, cartoons and traditional drawings. Posters promote concepts. Illustrations help them visualize success, the whole person, meeting Maslow's needs, themselves going through the stages and steps of recovery. They depict masks they wear and feelings underlying anger. People with limited language and/or academic skills often flourish through non-verbal communication.

8. **Written Projects** – De-emphasize spelling, grammar and neatness. Goal is freely expressing thoughts and feelings. Quizzes may be done individually or in teams. In dyads, they interview and record each other's response, then 'present' their partners to the group.

9. **Respect** – Before group elicit and reinforce these concepts: only one person at a time talks, no glamorizing alcohol, drugs, suicide, homicide, violence, promiscuity; everyone is entitled to an opinion; no put downs. Decide whether and in which circumstance profanity is allowed. It may be appropriate when giving an example of verbal aggression but is never tolerated toward staff or participants. No ethnic or racial slurs. Confidentiality prevails. People speak directly to each other, not through the leader. (They'll try. "She needs to …" or "He always…" Respond: "Tell him/her.")

10. **Avoid advice** – Encourage participants to be 'the voice of reason' for each other. Ask questions versus lecturing. If no one promotes an important precaution or concept, state it briefly with minimal elaboration. Later talk privately with the targets of your concern or develop an activity addressing the issue. Example: Rather than admonishing them about unprotected sex, set up a 'Doctor-Patient' or 'Dear Abby' or 'Talk Show' or 'Health Education' role-play wherein they take turns identifying risks and promoting celibacy or safe sex.

11. **Avoid power struggles** – Defiant people love to argue in front of an audience. If an issue is unimportant, let it go. People are free to express opposing views politely. If behavior is disruptive or disrespectful and verbal redirection is ineffective, the offender is asked to leave or escorted out and counseled privately. If people are reluctant to share thoughts or feelings, do not probe or try to force disclosure. Being allowed to 'pass' or to say something and 'let it rest' (versus being interrogated or listening to leader elaborating) empowers people. They'll open up sooner at their own pace.

12. **Do not expect perfection** – Participants may incorrectly or incompletely answer a question or explain a concept. Ask peers to challenge or augment the statement. Avoid intervening with lengthy explanations as they lose interest.

Tips To Bring Learning To Life
and Life To Learning

13. **"Too many cooks spoil the broth"** – Depending on the population, colleagues may need to be present. They should not answer questions for the participants or 'gang up' on someone. They often say what was 'on the tip of the tongue' of a participant. The facilitator may have an excellent reason for 'letting something slide'. When participants have exhausted all possibilities, facilitator may invite staff comments. Remember: The more talkative the professionals, the quieter and less involved are the participants.

    Picture this scenario: teens are effectively enlightening their peer who was passive-aggressive in sneaking out at night. A 'heavy' enters the room and reprimands her, "No wonder your parents don't trust you…" The participant shuts down. The peers slouch. They have been dwarfed by an authority figure. The momentum is destroyed.

14. **Set the stage, then get out of the way** – Your role is to plan the activity, prepare the props and materials, and whet their appetite for thinking, talking, doing. You are the 'prime mover.' You 'set the wheels in motion.' You may need to referee or keep them on track (unless their divergent direction is equally or more beneficial) but 'give them the ball and let them run with it.' You sit back and enjoy the show. Let the learning begin!

15. **Location, Location, Location** – if possible, do not have people too 'spread out.' Push tables together to promote eye contact and discussion. Exceptions: doing written work or an art project that warrants privacy and space. If possible, set chairs in a circle (no tables) fairly close for adults but farther apart for paranoid people or for young people (who tend to whisper and touch when too close). For game shows and teams, the chairs face each other in rows. A semicircle is useful for board work or for debates – the two opponents are in front, seen by all, and 'audience' members can see each other for discussion purposes. People generally achieve a comfort level by sitting in the same seat day after day. This should be allowed but can be modified to prove a point. Example: For a discussion about coping with change, put name labels on different chairs. Discuss how changes are usually uncomfortable, but we can adapt and benefit from them.

    Do not stand or sit behind a lectern or table – no barriers to communication. Avoid the traditional classroom set-up with Instructor at front and students facing him/her. When possible, place participants in the 'spotlight seat' or at the board. You take a 'back seat' among the members or 'audience'. The 'limelight' leads to learning!

TABLE OF CONTENTS

TABLE OF CONTENTS

ANGER MANAGEMENT

ANGER MANAGEMENT is crucial because suppressing or turning anger inward often leads to depression and self-harm. Escalating at slight provocations alienates and endangers others. Feeling angry is acceptable; threats or harm to self and/or others are unacceptable. Participants learn to handle antagonistic people and situations and to deal with underlying feelings.

ACTIVITY	PAGE NUMBERS	AGE	LEVEL OF DIFFICULTY	PAGES
Conflict Resolution	3 - 4	ALL	2	2
Don't Let Them Push Your Buttons	5 - 6	ALL	1	2
Passive, Aggressive, Assertive	7 - 9	ALL, *A, *YP	2	3
The Volcano	10 - 13	ALL, *A, *YP	2	4
Tic-Tac Anger	14 - 16	ALL	2	3
What's Going On With Them?	17 - 19	ALL, *A, *YP	1	3

LEGEND

AGES:

ALL = ALL ages, 8 or 9 through adults
YP = YOUNG PEOPLE, ages 8 or 9 through 17
T = TEENS, ages 13 through 17
A & T = ADULTS and TEENS, ages 13 and older
A = ADULTS, ages 18 and older
* = SPECIFIC PAGES expressly for this population.

LEVEL OF DIFFICULTY:

1 = EASIER - basic language; minimal reading and writing
2 = MODERATE - introduces new terminology; incorporates life experiences
3 = MORE DIFFICULT - requires some prior knowledge or introduction of new information; promotes peer teaching

PAGES:

The total number of pages related to the activity, including FACILITATOR'S INFORMATION and all accompanying pages.

CONFLICT RESOLUTION

AGE	DIFFICULTY	PAGES
ALL	2	2

PURPOSE

To practice conflict resolution steps.

MATERIALS

Board, marker, pencils, 'CONFLICT RESOLUTION' WORKSHEET, page 4.

ATTENTION GRABBER

Two people pantomime shouting, clenching fists, one walking out and slamming door or kicking a chair.
Ask group, "What was going on?" Ask, "What are ways to resolve conflict?"
Talking and time-out are often mentioned.
Explain that we will elaborate on these.

ACTIVITY

Volunteers write each conflict resolution step on board. Briefly, discuss each step.

Clear the air. ("We need to talk" or other 'opener.')
Time-out (if necessary) with a time limit. ("Let's wait one hour.")
Set ground rules. (No physical violence, no name calling, don't bring up the past or hit below the belt.)
Listen to the other side first. (Then they will be more receptive to your side.)
Summarize what opponent just said, incorporating feelings and/or reasons for his/her position.
Share own opinions and/or reasons.
Brainstorm all possible options.
Eliminate ridiculous or intolerable solutions.
Select a few preferable ones.
Weigh pros and cons of each.
Agree on a solution or sequence of solutions to try.
List possible 50/50 or 60/40 compromises.

FOLLOW-UP

Role-plays:
Two opponents sit at front.
Audience coaches them to take each step (from list on board).
Participants use actual conflicts they are currently facing with significant other.

VARIATION

Discuss the steps. Distribute worksheet. Participants answer and then share their responses OR pairs interview each other, document their partner's responses, then 'present' partner's situation to the group.

CONFLICT RESOLUTION

WORKSHEET

1. Clear the air. ("We need to talk" or other 'opener.')
2. Time-out (if necessary) with a time limit. ("Let's wait one hour.")
3. Set ground rules.
   (No physical violence, no name calling, don't bring up the past or hit below the belt.)
4. Listen to the other side first. (Then they will be more receptive to your side.)
5. Summarize what opponent just said, incorporating feelings and/or reasons for his/her position.
6. Share own opinions and/or reasons.
7. Brainstorm all possible options.
8. Eliminate ridiculous or intolerable solutions.
9. Select a few preferable ones.
10. Weigh pros and cons of each.
11. Agree on a solution or sequence of solutions to try.
12. List possible 50/50 or 60/40 compromises.

PLEASE ANSWER THESE QUESTIONS:

What is the purpose of 'time-out'? _____

What is 'hitting below the belt'? _____

Why should we summarize what opponent said? _____

What does 'brainstorm' mean? _____

What is a compromise? _____

Tell how you resolved a conflict in the past. _____

Tell about a current conflict you face:

    Who? _____

    What about? _____

    When did the problem start? _____

    When can you talk to the person? _____

    What does he or she want and why? _____

    What do you want and why? _____

    What compromises might work? _____

FACILITATOR'S INFORMATION
DON'T LET THEM PUSH YOUR BUTTONS

AGE	DIFFICULTY	PAGES
ALL	1	2

PURPOSE

Identify sources of agitation and prevent angry response.

MATERIALS

Board, marker, buttons, tape, paper, pencils,
'DON'T LET THEM PUSH YOUR BUTTONS' WORKSHEET, page 6.

ATTENTION GRABBER

Give a button to each person. Write on board, "Don't let them push your buttons."
Ask, "What does 'push my buttons' mean?"
Each person identifies what pushes his/her buttons.
(Examples: Criticism, people talking about my family, phoniness.)

ACTIVITY

Tape buttons to top of worksheets. Participants answer questions regarding most recent time they got really angry at a significant person. Elicit that our buttons get pushed because we allow it. We give someone the power and choose upsetting thoughts. Offer example: People call us "fatso" or unpleasant names. We're upset because we DECIDE to care about that opinion. Our esteem is threatened by being overweight and we think – "This is awful. They shouldn't call me names. I have to punch them." Alternatives: We can DECIDE "Name callers are ignorant and I don't want them as friends. They're cruel or insecure. I am worthwhile and attractive person regardless of my weight. It's unfortunate they said it but not the end of the world. Who is to say they 'shouldn't' do it? People do things they 'shouldn't' do all the time and I can't stop them. Punching them will get me in trouble. I can tell them how I feel, ask them to stop, tell someone in authority and decide to ignore them."

FOLLOW-UP

Participants discuss their worksheet answers.

VARIATION

PET PEEVES – people write their pet peeves anonymously on slips of paper – some may apply to peers. Put slips of paper in box. They take turns reading one, writing it on board, leading brainstorming sessions and listing ways to handle the person and/or peeve.

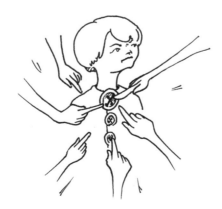

5

DON'T LET THEM PUSH YOUR BUTTONS

THE MOST RECENT TIME I WAS REALLY ANGRY AT A SIGNIFICANT PERSON:

<u>Who</u> was it?

<u>What</u> did this person do to 'push my buttons'?

<u>Where</u> did it occur?

<u>When</u>?

<u>Why</u> did this person do it? <u>Why</u> did it upset me?

<u>How</u> did I handle it?

<u>How</u> could I have <u>NOT</u> let this person 'push my buttons'?
(The other person's behavior is the same but I use different thoughts/feelings/actions in response.)

PASSIVE, AGGRESSIVE, ASSERTIVE

AGE	DIFFICULTY	PAGES
ALL *A *YP	2	3

PURPOSE

Discuss aggressive, passive, assertive and passive-aggressive behaviors and their outcomes. Practice assertion.

MATERIALS

Board, marker, container for CUT-UPS, small carpet, 'PASSIVE, AGGRESSIVE, ASSERTIVE' CUT-UPS, SITUATIONS for ADULTS, page 8, and SITUATIONS for YOUNG PEOPLE, page 9.

ATTENTION GRABBER

Place carpet near door. "What is this?"
Elicit – "doormat." Elicit/discuss that doormats get stepped on, stuff anger and explode or become depressed and/or harmful to themselves.
A participant writes on board "DOORMAT = PASSIVE." Volunteers write on board "EXPLODE = AGGRESSIVE", "SNEAKY = PASSIVE AGGRESSIVE" and "NICE BUT FIRM = ASSERTIVE."
Examples: "I feel...", "Please...", "No" and "Be honest."

ACTIVITY

Pass around container with CUT-UPS. They take turns reading a situation and giving an example of each response with its expected outcome. (They should recognize assertion as effective and the others as maladaptive.) This activity is preferable for hyperactive and/or gregarious people. See variation below for people exhibiting lethargy.

FOLLOW-UP

Personalize concepts by each group member:
1. telling a time s/he was passive, aggressive, passive-aggressive and assertive – and the outcomes.
2. role playing a current situation requiring assertion.

VARIATION

Use terms "STUFF", "ESCALATE", "SNEAKY", "HANDLE" – one on each of four walls. Tape bag with papers overflowing to one wall (STUFF); a picture of a tornado on the second wall (ESCALATE), a mask (SNEAKY) on the third wall; a diagram of a hand or handle on the fourth wall (HANDLE). When a situation is read, everyone goes to the wall representing his/her initial inclination. Each describes the behavior and its likely outcome. Let the 'handlers' be 'the voice of reason' – peers learn from them. If no one selected 'handle,' a volunteer must go to that wall/sign and describe assertive behavior and its benefits specific to the situation.

PASSIVE, AGGRESSIVE, ASSERTIVE

SITUATIONS for ADULTS

1 Your family disapproves of your partner.	**2** People behind you at the movies are talking loudly.	**3** You bought a defective product.	**4** Your car was repaired but continues to malfunction.
5 You are being physically, emotionally, sexually or financially abused.	**6** A friend calls during your favorite TV show.	**7** Your in-laws continually intrude.	**8** Your partner listens to phone calls or goes through your mail or personal belongings.
9 Your friend, family or partner continually puts you down.	**10** You want to be clean and sober but people push you to drink and/or use.	**11** People ask to borrow money or cigarettes or items you do not want to lend.	**12** People borrow and do not repay.
13 Friends want you to help them move and you do not want to injure your back.	**14** Someone asks about your age, weight, illness or other personal questions.	**15** You are unjustly accused of wrongdoing.	**16** Someone is flirting with your partner.
17 You think your partner may be having an affair.	**18** Your roommate or partner is sloppy.	**19** You want a new job, raise or promotion.	**20** A partner requests time alone.
21 A boss or co-worker takes credit for your idea.	**22** People (whose friendship you seek or with whom you must work) ignore you.	**23** You want to return to school or work and friends or family try to discourage you.	**24** Your partner, roommate or family does not help with household chores.
25 Your children are defiant and/or disobedient.	**26** You suspect your teenager is sexually active.	**27** You suspect your teenager drinks and/or uses drugs.	**28** Your kids dislike your partner or your partner dislikes your kids.

PASSIVE, AGGRESSIVE, ASSERTIVE

SITUATIONS for YOUNG PEOPLE

1 Someone borrows something and does not return it or breaks it.	**2** You are asked to baby-sit and the kid gets on your nerves.	**3** Someone cuts in front of you in line.	**4** Someone you dislike wants friendship or a relationship.
5 You want friendship or a relationship with someone who seems to ignore you.	**6** You want to be clean and sober and people are urging you to use drugs or drink alcohol.	**7** Someone cheats at a game.	**8** Someone asks to copy your answers on a test or homework.
9 You are asked your weight and don't want to tell.	**10** You do not understand a school assignment.	**11** Someone asks to borrow something you don't want to lend.	**12** Someone is listening to your phone conversation, reading your mail or going through your things.
13 You are called a nasty name.	**14** Someone takes your seat.	**15** Someone asks nosey questions about your family or your health/medication.	**16** Teachers or parents accuse you of something you did not do.
17 Someone is trying to turn your friend against you or trying to break-up a relationship.	**18** You are being emotionally, financially, physically or sexually abused.	**19** Someone tries to start a fight.	**20** Someone says mean things about you or your family.
21 You want to see a TV program or video and your friend or family wants to see another.	**22** People say you can't join their club, game or clique.	**23** People whisper, talk or laugh around you.	**24** It upsets you to see your parents fight.
25 Your parents have a substance abuse problem.	**26** Your grades are dropping.	**27** Friends want you to ditch school with them.	**28** You have trouble reading/writing and fear people will make fun of you.

FACILITATOR'S INFORMATION

THE VOLCANO

AGE	DIFFICULTY	PAGES
ALL *A *YP	2	4

PURPOSE

Identify feelings and/or issues underlying anger.

MATERIALS

Board, marker, paper, crayons, pencils, container for CUT-UPS.
For Follow-Up II, use 'THE VOLCANO' CUT-UPS, FOR ADULTS, page 12,
FOR YOUNG PEOPLE, page 13,
and 'THE VOLCANO' CARDS, page 11.

ATTENTION GRABBER

Show one member a picture of a volcano. S/he draws it on board and asks peers "What is this?"

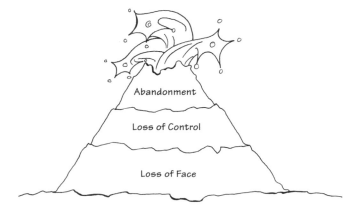

ACTIVITY

Discuss - Anger is the visible eruption of the volcano. Brainstorm and list the underlying feelings on board. Discuss three basic fears:
1. ABANDONMENT
2. LOSS OF CONTROL (of a situation or person)
3. LOSS OF FACE (feeling stupid or inadequate).

Have people share a time they were angry related to each fear and ways to cope. Ideas:
1. Recognize fear of ABANDONMENT, vulnerability to abuse just to avoid loneliness. Choose reliable people. Have more than one support person. Know when to end a relationship despite this fear.
2. To cope with LOSS OF CONTROL: Know we do control our body, thoughts, and feelings. Know our rights and practice assertion skills.
3. Ways to cope with fear of LOSS OF FACE: Know you may fear taking risks, speaking up, or trying new things (fear failure). Do reality checks – Realize "What people think is none of my business and can't hurt me." People who put us down are insecure themselves.

FOLLOW-UP

I. Participants draw the volcano with 3 sections underneath and write and depict situation(s) wherein they feared ABANDONMENT, LOSS OF CONTROL, LOSS OF FACE. Discuss better ways to handle each fear.

II. Each member gets 3 cards (page 11): one is labeled – 'FEAR OF ABANDONMENT', one is labeled – 'FEAR OF LOSS OF CONTROL' and one is labeled 'FEAR OF LOSS OF FACE'. Participants take turns reading the CUT-UPS exemplifying the fears. For each situation, people hold up the applicable card(s) and defend their selection. Opinions may vary. There are no right or wrong answers and some situations require all three cards.

THE VOLCANO

FEAR OF ABANDONMENT	FEAR OF ABANDONMENT
FEAR OF LOSS OF CONTROL	FEAR OF LOSS OF CONTROL
FEAR OF LOSS OF FACE	FEAR OF LOSS OF FACE

THE VOLCANO

FOR ADULTS

1 Your significant other leaves.	**2** You are fired or laid off.	**3** You are told you are not doing a good job.
4 You are turned down for a promotion.	**5** You cannot pay all your bills.	**6** You have been charged with a crime and must go to court.
7 You are diagnosed with a serious illness (physical or mental).	**8** Your significant other abuses you.	**9** You fail a test.
10 Your children disobey you.	**11** Your parents or in-laws move in with you.	**12** You are homeless.
13 A fire or disaster destroys all your possessions.	**14** You are robbed.	**15** A family member or friend dies.
16 You are raped or assaulted.	**17** Your wages are attached for debts or alimony.	**18** You are arrested.
19 You are in jail.	**20** The court orders mental health or substance abuse treatment.	**21** You have poor academic or job skills.
22 You have no friends.	**23** You have a drug or alcohol problem.	**24** You deal with being a minority.

THE VOLCANO

1 Your boyfriend or girlfriend leaves you.	**2** You are tied down in restraints.	**3** Someone calls you stupid or yells at you.
4 You fail a test.	**5** Your parents divorce.	**6** You are not selected for or thrown off a sport team.
7 Your parents restrict you from going out with your friends.	**8** Your roommate leaves or your best friend moves away.	**9** You are told you must obey rules.
10 One or both of your parents are far away or they die.	**11** Someone beats you or puts you down and you still try to be nice to them.	**12** Your boyfriend or girlfriend cheats on you.
13 Your best friend joins a group or club.	**14** Someone dares you to punch him / her.	**15** Your parents are always working or not at home.
16 Someone doesn't listen to your feelings.	**17** You lose an election at school.	**18** People make fun of you because you take medicine.
19 People say you are 'crazy'.	**20** You are put into a group home.	**21** You are told you can't eat snacks in your room.
22 You lose a game.	**23** You are physically, emotionally or sexually abused.	**24** You are given a time-out.

13

FACILITATOR'S INFORMATION
TIC-TAC-ANGER

AGE	DIFFICULTY	PAGES
ALL	2	3

PURPOSE

Identify anger management skills.

MATERIALS

Board, marker, pencils, 'TIC-TAC-ANGER' QUESTIONS, page 15, ANSWER SHEET for 'Game Show Host', page 16.
(Optional) prizes or play money (SKILLS BILLS, pages 277, 278).

ATTENTION GRABBER

Volunteer draws tic-tac-toe game on board.
Explain – Half the group are 'X', the others are 'O' – Teams sit facing each other.

ACTIVITY

'Game Show Host' draws Tic-Tac-Toe game on board. Two teams sit facing each other with 'Host' at board in front. At bottom of board note players' names under 'X' or 'O' and keep score (number of games won by each team). 'Host' asks alternate teams the questions; a correct answer warrants an 'X' or 'O'; teammates should collaborate on answers and some questions require two or more people to respond. If they answer incorrectly, the opposition tries. Continue until one team wins or all spaces are filled. If a tie occurs, the next question is the tie-breaker. Whichever team answers correctly first, wins. Erase board, appoint another 'Host' and continue until all questions have been answered. Winners get first choice of prizes; the opponents select from the remaining prizes. If no tangible rewards are available, discuss what everyone 'won' in terms of coping skills.

FOLLOW-UP

Each person tells one thing s/he learned and applies it to a current conflict.

VARIATION

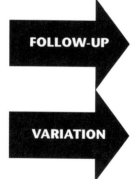

I. Considering group size and/or pre-knowledge of material, questions may be used in a discussion group format rather than as a game.

II. Distruibute questions only about fifteen minutes before game. Teams go to separate rooms or corners to discuss and note answers in advance.

TIC-TAC-ANGER

QUESTIONS

1. True or False – Another person can push your buttons.

2. Name one feeling underneath anger.

3. Name a wrong way to handle anger.

4. Tell three positive ways to handle anger.

5. What does it mean to act like a 'doormat'?

6. What happens to 'doormats'?

7. What is the opposite of a 'doormat'?

8. What happens to people who are aggressive?

9. What does assertive mean?

10. Give an example of an assertive statement.

11. Is it better to start a sentence with "I feel " or "You should"?

12. Why are "I" statements good?

13. Can we control what someone else says?

14. What is fear of abandonment?

15. Tell a time you got mad because you feared abandonment.

16. What is fear of loss of control?

17. Tell a time you were mad because you could not control a situation.

18. What is loss of face? Hint – it involves how you look to others.

19. Tell a time you were mad because you feared loss of face or looking like a fool.

20. Name two ways to handle fear of abandonment.

21. Name two ways to handle fear of loss of face.

22. Name two ways to handle fear of loss of control over people/situations.

Tic-Tac-Anger

ANSWER SHEET

1. True or False – Another person can push your buttons. *False*

2. Name one feeling underneath anger. *Fear, sadness, lonely*

3. Name a wrong way to handle anger. *Fist fights, stuff, self-harm, getting even*

4. Tell three positive ways to handle anger. *Talk, walk, time out, exercise, deep breathing*

5. What does it mean to act like a 'doormat'? *Passive – let people treat you badly*

6. What happens to 'doormats'? *Depression, suicide, self-mutilation, addiction*

7. What is the opposite of a 'doormat'? *Being aggressive/exploding*

8. What happens to people who are aggressive? *Relationship or legal problems*

9. What does assertive mean?
   State honest feelings firmly. Say no when necessary and ask for what you need.

10. Give an example of an assertive statement. *"I feel…" or "I'd appreciate it if you would…"*

11. Is it better to start a sentence with "I feel " or "You should"? *"I feel."*

12. Why are "I" statements good? *We have a right to state how we feel or what we want/need.*

13. Can we control what someone else says? *No*

14. What is fear of abandonment? *Afraid of being left alone*

15. Tell a time you got mad because you feared abandonment.

16. What is fear of loss of control?
    That someone has total control over you or you have no power over a situation.

17. Tell a time you were mad because you could not control a situation.

18. What is loss of face? Hint – it involves how you look to others.
    Thinking you look like a fool or a loser.

19. Tell a time you were mad because you feared loss of face or looking like a fool.

20. Name two ways to handle fear of abandonment.
    Recognize it. Talk to the person. Choose people who are loyal. Have a lot of support people.

21. Name two ways to handle fear of loss of face.
    *Realize what people think does not matter. Know that no one can make you look foolish.
    In any situation, failure is WINNING if you learn from it.*

22. Name two ways to handle fear of loss of control over people and/or situations.
    *Realize you cannot control other people. You can control your reaction. You can control who you
    hang out with and what situations you get into. You can ask for more independence. You can
    prove you can handle responsibility. You have a choice to leave a relationship or job that strips
    your power. You can select relationships, jobs and situations wherein you have equal power.*

FACILITATOR'S INFORMATION
"WHAT'S GOING ON WITH THEM?"

AGE	DIFFICULTY	PAGES
ALL *A *YP	1	3

PURPOSE

Develop empathy and avoid taking perceived affronts or attacks personally.

MATERIALS

Board, marker, container for CUT-UPS, pencils,
'WHAT'S GOING ON WITH THEM' CUT-UPS, FOR ADULTS, page 18
and FOR YOUNG PEOPLE, page 19.

ATTENTION GRABBER

Two volunteers, coached before group, role play a name-calling incident. Ask group – "What's going on?" Group members will probably assume the name-caller is mad at the other person. Ask, "What else could it be?" Elicit idea they could be displacing anger or putting someone down because they feel inferior (or other possibilities.)

ACTIVITY

Each reads one CUT-UP, and states what <u>could</u> be going on. Note: Purpose of this is <u>NOT</u> to encourage 'mind reading' or assumption but to avoid taking offense and to 'cut people some slack' who may have underlying issues or problems. Example: "Someone flips you off for no reason". Infer they are angry with someone or something else and avoid taking it personally. This activity fosters awareness of underlying reasons for behavior.

FOLLOW-UP

Discuss the 'bottom line' that we really do not know what motivates behavior but should not take things personally, become insulted or retaliate. If possible, we need to ask the person what is going on (do reality checks). Emphasize that most people are doing the best they can despite the appearance of 'bad' behavior.

VARIATION

Keep CUT-UP page intact. Distribute as a worksheet. Individuals, dyads or teams write brief answers, then reconvene as whole group and compare responses.

17

"What's Going On With Them?"

1 They brag about their looks, love life or accomplishments.	**2** They constantly criticize you.	**3** They frequently tell dirty jokes.
4 They yell or snap at you when you've done nothing wrong.	**5** They give you the 'silent treatment'.	**6** Your partner withholds money or sex.
7 They're angry because you spend time with family, friends or other interests.	**8** Your boss does not compliment a job well done.	**9** Significant others ignore or minimize your accomplishments.
10 A person close to you 'clams-up'.	**11** They flaunt money or possessions.	**12** Your co-worker is not doing his/her 'fair share' of the work.
13 Your co-worker is often late or absent.	**14** Someone blames you for a mistake he or she made.	**15** A significant other requests time alone.
16 Someone forgot something very important you recently revealed.	**17** A co-worker or boss takes credit for your ideas.	**18** People ignore you.

18

"WHAT'S GOING ON WITH THEM?"

FOR YOUNG PEOPLE

1 They brag about how smart they are.	**2** They always flex their muscles.	**3** They flip people off for no reason.
4 They make funny faces.	**5** They laugh when serious topics are discussed.	**6** They put other people down.
7 They are real quiet.	**8** They are real loud.	**9** They act like they know it all.
10 They call people names.	**11** They get mad when they lose a game.	**12** They talk real tough.
13 They give people dirty looks.	**14** They talk about people behind their backs.	**15** They steal food.
16 They do disgusting things like smearing boogers on tables.	**17** They always tell dirty jokes.	**18** They constantly cuss.

19

ASSERTION

ASSERTION is imperative because passivity destroys self-determination, leading to helpless, hopeless resignation and /or eventual aggression. Participants practice stating their needs, defending opinions, saying "No", and differentiating among passive, aggressive and assertive responses.

ACTIVITY	PAGE NUMBERS	AGE	LEVEL OF DIFFICULTY	PAGES
Debates	23 - 24	A & T	2	2
Just Do It	25 - 27	ALL	1	3
Opinions	28 - 29	A & T	2	2
Stand Up For Your Beliefs	30 - 31	A & T	2	2
Tell It Like It Is	32	ALL	1	1

LEGEND

AGES:
ALL = ALL ages, 8 or 9 through adults
YP = YOUNG PEOPLE, ages 8 or 9 through 17
T = TEENS, ages 13 through 17
A & T = ADULTS and TEENS, ages 13 and older
A = ADULTS, ages 18 and older
* = SPECIFIC PAGES expressly for this population.

LEVEL OF DIFFICULTY:
1 = EASIER - basic language; minimal reading and writing
2 = MODERATE - introduces new terminology; incorporates life experiences
3 = MORE DIFFICULT - requires some prior knowledge or introduction of new information; promotes peer teaching

PAGES:
The total number of pages related to the activity, including FACILITATOR'S INFORMATION and all accompanying pages.

FACILITATOR'S INFORMATION

DEBATES

AGE	DIFFICULTY	PAGES
A & T	2	2

PURPOSE

To practice defending beliefs despite opposition.

MATERIALS

Board, marker, pencils, paper, container for cut-ups, and 'DEBATES' CUT-UPS, page 24. (Optional) two podiums, tape, signs for PROPONENT and OPPONENT.

ATTENTION GRABBER

Volunteer writes PROPONENT on one side of board, OPPONENT on other side and DISCUSSION in the middle, or tapes PROPONENT and OPPONENT signs on podiums and writes DISCUSSION on board (to be used for questions 13,14,16,17,19, 20 of 'DEBATES' QUESTIONS, page 24, which are not relevant to 'for or against' responses). Volunteer asks, "What do these words mean?"

ACTIVITY

Explain, "We are having debates." Discuss and list rules such as three minutes for each side, one-minute rebuttals, no profanity or 'put-downs', and 'audience' must maintain eye contact and silence.

Volunteer selects a topic from cut-ups, decides on position, and stands under PROPONENT or OPPONENT on board or at podium. A peer takes the other side. If topic applies to DISCUSSION instead, two people stand under DISCUSSION, stating and substantiating their views. When debaters are finished, 'audience' provides feedback.

The process is repeated with new topics and different debaters.

FOLLOW-UP

Ask, "Is it ok to change your mind after considering all aspects?" (Yes!) Participants share about times they altered their opinions and times they firmly defended their beliefs.

VARIATION

People select topics about fifteen minutes before debates and outline their arguments in advance.

23

DEBATES

QUESTIONS (for each explain why/why not):

1 Should marijuana be legalized?	**2** Should alcoholic beverages be illegal?	**3** Should prayer be allowed in school?	**4** Should school teach sex education?
5 Should abortion be legal?	**6** Should rapists be castrated?	**7** Should gays/lesbians be allowed to marry?	**8** Should gays/lesbians be allowed to adopt children?
9 Should people live together before marriage?	**10** Should smoking be allowed in public buildings or restaurants?	**11** Should people on welfare be forced to work?	**12** Should capital punishment be banned?
13 What are the top three priorities for federal spending?	**14** How can the health care system be improved?	**15** Should more money be spent on space exploration?	**16** How much time should children spend watching TV and playing video games?
17 Is the environment or the economy more important? (Assume a company employing thousands in your town may be shut down due to pollution.)	**18** Should rock music be censored?	**19** How can prisoners be rehabilitated?	**20** How can we help the homeless?

FACILITATOR'S INFORMATION

AGE	DIFFICULTY	PAGES
ALL	1	3

PURPOSE

Practice assertion.

MATERIALS

Board, marker, container for CUT-UPS, 'JUST DO IT' CUT-UPS, page 26.
Pencils, clipboards and 'JUST DO IT' CHECKLIST, page 27, for VARIATION.

ATTENTION GRABBER

Volunteer writes 'Just do it!' on board.
Discuss times they have taken a challenging step.

ACTIVITY

Each selects a CUT-UP and role-plays (alone or with peer assistance.)
Group members provide feedback.

FOLLOW-UP

Each tells a positive action s/he needs to 'just do.'

VARIATION

This gets people who act tired or shy to move and mingle. Each receives check-off sheet, clipboard and pencil. Move all chairs to perimeter of room. They move freely around room performing required tasks with various peers. Those who assist with role-plays initial each other's sheets. They are not to pair-up but do different actions with different people.

Just Do It!

1 Receive and refuse an invitation.	**2** Make a request.	**3** Express fear.	**4** Express anger (assertively, not aggressively.)
5 Introduce yourself.	**6** Give a compliment.	**7** State a decision without justifying it.	**8** Express love.
9 Ask to borrow something.	**10** Receive a compliment.	**11** Receive constructive criticism.	**12** Give constructive criticism.
13 Say "No" to a request.	**14** Start a conversation.	**15** Receive an invitation and accept.	**16** Express annoyance. (Use an "I" statement)
17 Express an opinion.	**18** Say "I don't know" without apologizing.	**19** Admit a mistake and accept the consequences.	**20** Say something positive about yourself.

26

CHECKLIST

ACTIONS	WITNESS INITIALS
Receive and refuse and invitation.	
Make a request.	
Express fear.	
Express anger (assertively, not aggressively).	
Introduce yourself.	
Give a compliment.	
Receive a compliment.	
State a decision without justifying it.	
Express love.	
Ask to borrow something.	
Receive constructive criticism.	
Give constructive criticism.	
Say "No" to a request.	
Start a conversation.	
Receive an invitation and accept.	
Express annoyance. (Use an "I" statement)	
Express an opinion	
Say "I don't know" without apologizing.	
Admit a mistake and accept the consequences.	
Say something positive about yourself.	

FACILITATOR'S INFORMATION

AGE	DIFFICULTY	PAGES
A & T	2	2

PURPOSE Identify and express thoughts. Peer teaching.

MATERIALS Board, marker, papers, pencils, 'OPINIONS' QUESTIONS, page 29.

ATTENTION GRABBER Ask "Has anyone made a speech? About what? How did you feel?"
Explain: "Today we will express our opinions and teach each other."
Discuss rules – eye contact, listen until speech is over, raise hands for questions and/or comments after each speech.

ACTIVITY People select a question from the OPINIONS list and take 5-10 minutes to prepare (make notes).
Then each presents his/her opinion.
Audience asks questions and gives feedback.

FOLLOW-UP Discuss how it felt to express an opinion.
Describe comfort level when challenged by audience's questions.

QUESTIONS

1 . Can an alcoholic or addict drink or use just a little?

2 . Who is responsible for my happiness (unhappiness) and how?

3 . How can I cut down on paranoia?

4 . How much power do I give the past over the present and how can I give the past less power?

5 . How do I handle anxiety and how can I improve?

6 . How do I handle anger and how can I improve?

7 . How do my thoughts affect my feelings and actions?

8 . How has this been true for me? "I get what I expect."

9 . What does "Live and Let Live" mean?

10 . How do I deal with change and how can I handle it better?

11 . Are my thoughts or feelings in the driver's seat and how does this affect me?

12 . What does "First Things First" mean to me, and what are my top five priorities?

13 . How could a serious disease affect my life negatively and positively?

14 . What does it mean to 'act as if'? Name three situations where this will help me.

15 . How can I control my thoughts, feelings and actions?

16 . What steps do I take to fight depression?

17 . How can I get more love in my life?

18 . How do people overcome addiction?

19 . Is there safe sex? Why? or why not?

20. When does alcohol use become abuse?

FACILITATOR'S INFORMATION

STAND UP FOR YOUR BELIEFS

AGE	DIFFICULTY	PAGES
A & T	2	2

PURPOSE ▶ Practice asserting and defending beliefs.

MATERIALS ▶ Board, marker, signs for wall YES and NO,
'STAND UP FOR YOUR BELIEFS' CUT-UPS, page 31, tape.

ATTENTION GRABBER ▶ One volunteer nods head as in charades. Participants are asked – "What is s/he saying?"
That person tapes YES sign to one wall. Another person tapes the NO sign to opposite wall.
Chairs are in center of room.

ACTIVITY ▶ Take turns selecting CUT-UP. Write statement on board. Everyone goes to one side or the other.
Take turns defending reasons for YES or NO. All must respect each other's beliefs – debating is
not allowed as purpose is to take a risk and state beliefs without fear of being chastised or
mocked. Many may say they are 'in the middle' and have reasons for both YES and NO. They
must first stand under one sign and then the other as they argue for or against the statement
(they are still practicing asserting and defending their beliefs).

FOLLOW-UP ▶ Discuss how it felt to take a stand for beliefs.

STAND UP FOR YOUR BELIEFS

QUESTIONS

1 Should parents spank their children?	**2** Should parents argue in front of children?	**3** Can an alcoholic learn to drink in moderation?	**4** Should everyone of legal age always vote?
5 Should teachers be allowed to go on strike?	**6** Should doctors and nurses be allowed to go on strike?	**7** Should children be allowed to picket their school?	**8** Should children be allowed to boycott their school?
9 Should obese teens be cheerleaders?	**10** Should kids with failing grades be allowed to play school sports?	**11** Should repeated rapists or kidnappers be jailed for life?	**12** Should the government provide private school vouchers?
13 Should the President's personal life concern the citizens?	**14** Should earnings of sports figures, music or movie stars be capped?	**15** Are sports figures or politicians good role models?	**16** Should alimony be paid to a woman who is capable of working?
17 Should clean needles be distributed to addicts?	**18** Should condoms be distributed by schools?	**19** Should people be forced to retire at a certain age?	**20** Should SSI or disability checks be paid to substance abusers?

FACILITATOR'S INFORMATION
Tell It Like It Is

AGE	DIFFICULTY	PAGES
ALL	1	1

PURPOSE

To practice assertion skills.

MATERIALS

Board, marker, paper labeled "NERVY", paper labeled "WIMPY", and tape; pencils and paper or index cards for FOLLOW-UP.

ATTENTION GRABBER

Two volunteers, coached before group, tape labels to their chests and role-play.

NERVY: "Will you help me move five rooms of furniture this weekend?"
WIMPY: "Sure, I'd love to."
NERVY leaves the room.
WIMPY, with disgusted facial expression, exclaims, "Oh no! Look what I've gotten myself into. I wish I said no."

ACTIVITY

Ask, "What happened in the role-play?" Encourage sharing about times participants have acted 'wimpy'. Examples: saying "yes" when they wanted to say "no", not expressing an opinion, giving into peer pressure, failure to ask for something they need. Ask, "Why do we act wimpy sometimes?" (fear rejection, avoid conflict, prevent hurting someone's feelings)

Volunteer writes: TELL IT LIKE IT IS on board. Explain, "We're going to practice this."

Volunteer writes: #1 - THINK FIRST on board. Discuss importance of evaluating the situation, our thoughts, feelings and rights. Ask "Are there times when we should go with the flow?" (Yes. Examples: someone has a weapon; the police or other authority figures are giving orders in an emergency; an established rule cannot be changed at the moment.)

Volunteer writes #2 - ACKNOWLEDGE on board. Discuss value of recognizing the request. Examples: "You need help moving.", "Your opinion is… ", " You want me to drink with you.", "Your needs are…"

Volunteer writes:#3 - SPEAK YOUR MIND on board. Discuss and list examples: "I feel…", "I think…", "I need…", "No."

Volunteer writes: #4 - STAND YOUR GROUND on board. Discuss value of repeating the exact words spoken in #3, calmly but firmly. Elicit that it shows you 'mean business'. Emphasize and note on board: "Do not elaborate or make excuses!"

Volunteer writes #5 - SAY NO AND GO. Discuss value of 'no and go' when others refuse to respect your rights or recognize your responses (numbers 2,3, and 4 above).

FOLLOW-UP

Two participants at a time sit in 'spotlight seats' and role-play anticipated situations wherein they'll be challenged by 'nervy' people, peer pressure, unreasonable requests by loved ones or wherein they must make own needs known. The 'audience' coaches them through the steps (listed on board).

Participants copy the steps on wallet-size slips of paper or index cards, practice in 'real life', and report to group a few days later. They keep list of steps on mirror, in wallet or other accessible location.

COGNITIVE CHANGES

COGNITIVE CHANGES can save and improve quality of life. Negative distortions that ruin relationships and self-concept and are identified. Participants substitute positive but realistic thoughts with resultant revisions in emotions and behavior.

ACTIVITY	PAGE NUMBERS	AGE	LEVEL OF DIFFICULTY	PAGES
Commercials and Posters	35	ALL	1	1
Distorted Thinking Role Plays	36 - 39	A & T	2	4
Don't Jump to Conclusions	40 - 42	ALL, * A, * YP	1	3
M and M's (Misery Makers)	43 - 44	A & T	1	2
No Dumping	45 - 46	ALL	1	2
Over the Hump	47	ALL	1	1
Stinking Thinking	48 - 49	ALL	1	2
TFA	50 - 51	ALL	1	2
Untangle Your Thinking	52 - 53	A & T	2	2
What's the Point	54 - 55	A & T	2	2
You are What You Do	56 - 57	ALL	1	2
Zappers	58 - 59	ALL	1	2

LEGEND

AGES:
ALL = ALL ages, 8 or 9 through adults
YP = YOUNG PEOPLE, ages 8 or 9 through 17
T = TEENS, ages 13 through 17
A & T = ADULTS and TEENS, ages 13 and older
A = ADULTS, ages 18 and older
* = SPECIFIC PAGES expressly for this population.

LEVEL OF DIFFICULTY:
1 = EASIER - basic language; minimal reading and writing
2 = MODERATE - introduces new terminology; incorporates life experiences
3 = MORE DIFFICULT - requires some prior knowledge or introduction of new information; promotes peer teaching

PAGES:
The total number of pages related to the activity, including FACILITATOR'S INFORMATION and all accompanying pages.

COMMERCIALS AND POSTERS

AGE	DIFFICULTY	PAGES
ALL	1	1

PURPOSE

Creatively express and promote healthy messages.
Initially participants may not value medication, sobriety, support groups or other concepts.
By going through the motions of convincing others via art, drama, humor, slogans, etc., they
    start believing it themselves.
They are 'acting as if' or acting their way into appropriate attitudes.

MATERIALS

Paper, pencils, crayons, magazines for collages and a poster or magazine advertisement (for
example). Video or instant cameras add excitement if they are allowed and/or available.
Safe snub-nose scissors for collages (be sure to reclaim after group).

ATTENTION GRABBER

Show poster or magazine ad.
Ask the purpose of posters and commercials.

ACTIVITY

Participants select an idea to 'sell' and they work in dyads, small groups,
or individually to role play, create a monologue, poem or a poster.

Themes might be:
    Benefits of prescribed medicines and therapy
    Benefits of sobriety
    Value of support groups
    Value of 12-step work
    Anger management techniques
    Mood boosters
    How to survive break up or divorce
    Starting a new school or job
Participants share their 'acts', poems or posters and receive feedback.

FOLLOW-UP

Discuss: how their beliefs and/or feelings were strengthened by the activity.
Discuss: "Talk the talk and soon you'll walk the walk."

DISTORTED THINKING ROLE PLAYS

AGE	DIFFICULTY	PAGES
A & T	2	4

PURPOSE

Identify distortions and their effects.

MATERIALS

Board, marker, container for CUT-UPS,
LIST OF DISTORTIONS FOR PARTICIPANTS, page 37,
and 'DISTORTED THINKING ROLE PLAYS' CUT-UPS, page 38.
See 'FOR FACILITATOR'S EYES ONLY', page 39,
linking distortions to the role of group leader.

ATTENTION GRABBER

Two volunteers (coached before group) role play one situation. Ask: "What's going on?"
Elicit concept: We often negatively misinterpret. Write "Distorted Thinking" on board.

ACTIVITY

Distribute photocopy of 'LIST OF DISTORTIONS FOR PARTICIPANTS' to each person.
Take turns writing the distortions on board and discussing their meanings:
    Emotional Reasoning
    Blaming
    Shoulds
    Fortune Telling
    Mind Reading
    Jumping to Conclusions
    Magnifying Negatives
    Minimizing Positives
    Filtering (focusing on negatives)
    Overgeneralization
    Labeling
    Personalization
    Catastrophizing
    Polarized, Black & White, All or Nothing Thinking.
Pass around container with CUT-UPS.
Each pair picks a role-play and practices (in separate corners or rooms),
    then role-plays for 'audience.'
'Audience' guesses the distortion being portrayed from the list on board.
All discuss more positive but plausible explanations for the situation.

FOLLOW-UP

Each shares a time s/he experienced each distortion and how s/he recognized the truth.

DISTORTED THINKING ROLE PLAYS

LIST of DISTORTIONS for PARTICIPANTS

All or Nothing / Black and White / Polarized Thinking: You think you're good or bad, smart or dumb, a winner or a loser. You need to see 'shades of gray' or 'the middle ground'. No one is 100% successful in everything. Everyone has assets and limitations.

Overgeneralization: Because something seems negative, you assume everything will always go wrong. You got a failing grade and decide you'll never graduate. Someone breaks up with you and you decide you'll never have a satisfying relationship.

Filtering (focusing on negative): You focus on the rubbish (like coffee grounds) and ignore the positives (the flavorful brew). You get 2-A's, 2-B's, and a D. Instead of praising yourself for A's and B's, you torture yourself over the D.

Jumping to Conclusions / Mind Reading / Fortune Telling: You immediately assume the worst. You think you can read minds. People are whispering or laughing and you know it's about you. You think you're a fortuneteller. "I'll never get promoted."

Catastrophizing or Magnifying Negatives or Minimizing Positives: You decide a small setback is a major catastrophe. You were reprimanded at work and are sure you'll be fired. You magnify your faults or the potential pitfalls of a situation and minimize your assets and achievements. You magnify others' attributes and ignore your own.

Emotional Reasoning: You allow feelings to guide your thoughts. You are depressed and decide life is hopeless. If your moods are governed by a chemical imbalance, they are unpredictable and inaccurate.

Shoulds: Also known as 'Musts', 'Oughts', and 'Shouldn'ts'. You pressure or chastise yourself and others. Who has authority to dictate someone's behavior? You set yourself up for failure or anger. Don't 'should' on yourself or others.

Labeling: You call yourself, or others, names like "incompetent", "ignorant", "crazy", or "lazy". Labels stick in your mind and cause you to give up on yourself, others, relationships and/or situations.

Personalization: You take something personally that is marginally relevant to you. You're late to work two times. When a memo is distributed about tardiness, you believe it's meant for you alone (forgetting that numerous co-workers come late).

Blaming Others: You blame others for your joy or misery. "If only he'd ask me out I'd be happy", "It's all her fault I'm in a bad mood." What others say or do affects you only with your permission. Happiness is an 'inside job' contingent on your view of self and/or circumstances.
Blaming Self: You take responsibility for people's actions and/or situations beyond your control.

To learn more about distorted thinking, consult:
  <u>Ten Days to Self-Esteem</u>, by David D. Burns, M.D., © 1993, NY, William Morrow and Company, Inc.

DISTORTED THINKING ROLE PLAYS

Role plays (Audience guesses the negative distortion.) Suggested answers are in parenthesis but others may be correct.

1

Person A says "Hello". Person B ignores him/her. Person A assumes "S/he hates me." (Jumping to Conclusions or Mind Reading)

2

Boss tells worker, "You have made great progress and are ready for a promotion." Worker says: "It's nothing – s/he's just saying that." (Minimizing positives)

3

A guy asks girl for date. She says she is busy. Guy thinks, "No one will ever want me." (Fortune Telling, Overgeneralization)

4

Interviewer turns person down for a job. Person assumes, "I'll never get hired." (Overgeneralization & Fortune Telling)

5

Boss tells worker, "You made a mistake." Worker states, "I'm getting fired." (Catastrophizing)

6

Person trips and says, "I'm a clumsy clod." (Labeling)

7

A man swears, a woman says, "All men have filthy mouths." A woman cries, a man says, "All women are cry babies." (Overgeneralizing, Labeling, All or Nothing)

8

Student gets report card – four B's and one D in History – "I'm stupid because of the D." (Filtering and focusing on negatives, All or Nothing)

9

Lover smiles at someone and partner says, "S/he's going to cheat." (Fortune Telling and Jumping to Conclusions)

10

Coach: "You did well in the game." Player: "No, I didn't." (Minimizing positives)

11

Person compliments a friend who responds: "S/he wants something." (Mind Reading)

12

Teacher says, "You need help with reading". Student: "I'm an idiot." (Magnifying, Overgeneralizing, Labeling)

13

"I must lose weight, I must get my GED, I have to get a job tomorrow, or I have to have a wife/husband." (Shoulds)

14

"I feel like a failure so I must be one." (Emotional Reasoning)

15

Teenage daughter tells mother she is pregnant. Mother thinks, "It's all my fault." (Blaming Self)

16

"If I pass the test, I'm smart. If I fail, I'm dumb." (Polarized/Black & White or All or Nothing Thinking, Labeling, Overgeneralization)

17

"If I'm married, I'm lovable. If someone breaks up with me, I'm worthless." (Labeling, Polarized/Black & White or All or Nothing Thinking, Overgeneralization)

18

Doctor: "We need to repeat your mammogram." Woman: "I've got breast cancer." (Catastrophizing)

19

Teen tells parent, "I had a little accident." Parent: "S/he totaled the car. S/he was drunk." (Catastrophizing, Jumping to Conclusions)

20

New worker is ignored by co-workers and says: "I'll never make friends here." (Fortune Telling)

21

Wife looks at watch. "My husband is an hour late. He must have gotten killed in a crash." (Catastrophizing)

38

DISTORTED THINKING FOR FACILITATOR'S EYES ONLY!

Cognitive therapy teaches people to identify, refute, and replace distorted negative thoughts. They learn that thoughts influence feelings and actions. This sheet helps facilitators understand distortions in context of their jobs and/or roles. Please use the 'LIST OF DISTORTIONS FOR PARTICIPANTS', page __, when conducting the group!

Situation: You lead a group and some participants seem bored or belligerent.
     Thought – "I'll never do a decent group"
     Feeling – useless, hopeless
     Action – hide in your office

Cognitive Distortions

All or Nothing – (also known as polarized or black and white) If you are not perfect you are a total failure. You are good or bad, smart or dumb, energetic or lazy. (You must learn to think in 'shades of gray'.)

Overgeneralization – because one group went poorly, you decide you will always fail.

Mental filter – you focus on the rubbish or the negatives (like coffee grounds) versus focusing on all the positives of a situation. Maybe only a few people were disinterested, but you rate your performance by them.

Jumping to conclusions – you interpret things negatively via mind reading ("They're bored" when perhaps their medications sedated them) or fortune telling ("I'll never run an exciting group").

Catastrophizing or Magnifying or Minimizing – you think it is the end of your career because a group activity was a dud or you mentally inflate your colleague's capabilities and minimize your own.

Emotional reasoning – because you feel worthless, that means you are.

Shoulds – also 'shouldn'ts', 'musts', 'oughts' – you either unduly pressure yourself or try to dictate someone's behavior – "I should do a great group every time" or "He shouldn't talk back". You set yourself up for failure or anger. (Don't 'should' on yourself or anybody else!)

Labeling – you call yourself 'incompetent' or 'ignorant' because of a series of events that weren't your fault. You decide a person who disagrees is 'defiant'.

Personalization/Blaming – you blame yourself for a less than lively group. Perhaps members were coming down with the flu or preoccupied with hallucinations.

After identifying the distortions, people need to invalidate the thought by asking others and looking at facts (shades of gray or percents). In reality, you probably run great groups seven out of ten times. When negative thoughts are replaced by more positive but realistic ones, feelings and actions are more productive. Note that the original situation does not change:

    Situation – you lead a group and some participants seem bored or belligerent.

Thought	"Some people looked bored or seemed argumentative."
Feeling	Disappointed, concerned
Action	You look for possible reasons unrelated to you. (The members were tired or angry at someone else).
	You look for ways to spice up your next group (make the sloucher the 'Game Show Host' or encourage quarrelsome people to lead a debate).
	You decide it is healthy for participants to challenge you and teach the value of assertion versus aggression.
	You try again, versus avoiding groups.

Please note: In the activities, do not 'split hairs' over which distortion is exemplified. Some situations encompass several. Recognizing that distortions exist and replacing them with more positive and realistic thoughts is the goal.

To learn more about cognitive changes, consult:
<u>Ten Days to Self-Esteem</u>, by David D. Burns, M.D., ©1993, NY, William Morrow and Company, Inc.

FACILITATOR'S INFORMATION
DON'T JUMP TO CONCLUSIONS

AGE	DIFFICULTY	PAGES
ALL *A *YP	1	3

PURPOSE

To practice a positive or neutral initial reaction versus assuming the worst.

MATERIALS

Board, marker, container for CUT-UPS,
'DON'T JUMP TO CONCLUSIONS' CUT-UPS, FOR ADULTS, page 41,
and FOR YOUNG PEOPLE, page 42.

ATTENTION GRABBER

Volunteers practice before group, then role-play this scenario:
  Guy: "Would you like to go out for dinner tonight?"
  Girl: "No, I'm sorry. I've made other plans."

Ask participant what the guy's first thought might be. Most will assume he'll feel rejected. Ask what he'll probably do. Most will reply he'll give up. Ask what might be the truth about the situation and elicit that she may actually be busy tonight, would love to go out with him, and he would have missed a great date because he jumped to the worst conclusion.

Volunteer prints the word ASSUME on board. Ask, "What happens when we assume things?" If group members are casual adults, someone may point out, (or leader may elicit), that assumptions make an "ass of you and me" as indicated in the spelling: **ass/u/me**. Ask for examples of times they jumped to negative or erroneous conclusions.

ACTIVITY

Explain "We're going to think about situations where people might assume the worst and practice taking things at face value. This container has slips of paper with situations written on them. When it's your turn, pick one, read the situation aloud, tell the first negative assumption you or others might make. Then take it at face value and think of a positive or neutral explanation." They take turns answering; if anyone has difficulty, encourage peer assistance.

FOLLOW-UP

Each shares the most recent time s/he jumped to conclusions and the results. Each shares a time someone jumped to negative conclusions about something s/he said or did and the consequences.

DON'T JUMP TO CONCLUSIONS

FOR ADULTS

1 They keep looking at their watch when you're talking.	**2** Your partner starts working late.	**3** Your work performance evaluation is late.
4 Your partner fails to call or show-up for a date.	**5** Someone cancels a date.	**6** You are called into the doctor's office to discuss test results.
7 You are informed of an appointment with your probation officer.	**8** You are called into the Human Resources office about your job.	**9** A store security officer looks at you.
10 You are selected for an Internal Revenue Service audit.	**11** You are asked if you know anything about someone's missing money or property.	**12** You are pulled over by the police.

41

DON'T JUMP TO CONCLUSIONS

FOR YOUNG PEOPLE

1 Your teacher asks to speak with you after class.	**2** People are whispering or laughing.	**3** People are looking at your new outfit or hairstyle.
4 You sit down to eat your lunch and soon others at the table leave.	**5** You call a friend who states, "I can't talk right now".	**6** Someone refuses an invitation to go someplace with you because they already have other plans.
7 Your parents say, "We need to talk".	**8** School police or store security officers are looking at you.	**9** Your parents ask whether you drink or use drugs.
10 Someone gives you a compliment; someone gives you constructive criticism.	**11** You are asked if you know anything about someone's missing money or belongings.	**12** A police officer walks up to you.

M AND M'S

AGE	DIFFICULTY	PAGES
A & T	1	2

PURPOSE

Recognize and refute 'Misery Makers' (negative or irrational thoughts).

MATERIALS

Board, marker, container for CUT-UPS, 'Misery Makers', 'M AND M' CUT-UPS, page 44, paper cups filled with appropriate candy.

Examples: I must please everyone all the time.
  If I don't succeed at this (test, job, relationship, etc.), I'm worthless.
  I must always win. I must always be the best.
  If 'X' doesn't love or approve of me, I'm worthless.

ATTENTION GRABBER

Show cup and candy. Ask what the candy is called.
Someone write 'M and M's' on the board, then write M _ _ _ _ _ M _ _ _ _ _ and have group guess letters (Misery Makers).

ACTIVITY

Discuss "What kind of thoughts are 'Misery Makers'?" Ask for examples. Write them on the board and ask why each is a 'Misery Maker' (relate to perfectionism or unrealistic goals of 100% approval) and practice refuting the statements.
Participants take turns selecting CUT-UPS, copying the 'Misery Makers' onto board and sitting in the 'spotlight seat'. They tell why it's irrational and restate it in a positive but realistic manner. They elicit help from peers as needed.
Each receives a cup of candy when leaving the 'spotlight seat'.

FOLLOW-UP

Personalize concepts: each shares a current 'misery maker' thought, tells why it is negative and/or irrational and restates it in positive and/or realistic terms.

M AND M'S

MISERY MAKERS

1 If my lover, spouse, _____ leaves me, I'm unlovable or worthless.

2 I need everybody's approval.

3 I must be perfect in everything I do.

4 Events, people, places and things cause my misery.

5 Avoidance is easier than facing problems.

6 My past will ruin my whole life.

7 I can't help it if I feel depressed.

8 I must never hurt someone's feelings.

9 I must never refuse a request.

10 If someone criticizes me, they are right and I'd better change.

11 I must give 95% in a relationship.

12 If I'm alone, I must be lonely.

13 I will someday find the perfect friend, lover, job, _____.

14 Feeling angry is bad.

15 Selfishness is never necessary.

16 If I fail at a job, test, relationship or _____ I'm a failure.

17 I must avoid all anxiety producing situations.

18 Getting older is terrible.

19 If I wasn't loved as a child, I'm ruined.

20 If I was abused, I'm ruined.

21 I can't forgive _____.

22 I messed up before and history always repeats itself.

FACILITATOR'S INFORMATION
No Dumping

AGE	DIFFICULTY	PAGES
ALL	1	2

PURPOSE ▶ Identify and change 'trash thoughts'.

MATERIALS ▶ Board, marker, paper, pencils, waste basket with clean crumpled papers, 'NO DUMPING' CUT-UPS, page 46.
(Photocopy and cut in half. Each half for one negative thought.)
Crayons, magazines, snub-nosed scissors and tape or glue for VARIATION.

ATTENTION GRABBER ▶ Volunteer walks into room and empties wastebasket onto floor.
Ask, "What did s/he do?"
Volunteer writes, 'No Dumping' on board.
Ask how this relates to our thoughts.
(Elicit concept: negative thoughts are trash.)

ACTIVITY ▶ Participants write negative thoughts on CUT-UP pages, then crumple and throw papers into wastebasket. Dump them onto table or floor. Take turns uncrumpling a page, writing the 'trash thought' on board, and replacing it with a more positive but realistic thought.

FOLLOW-UP ▶ Discuss how we can say 'No Dumping' to ourselves and refuse to entertain thoughts that depress, lower our esteem or lead to anger, drinking, drugs, resentment.

VARIATION ▶
I. Discuss being 'down in the dumps' due to negative thoughts, feelings and actions and how to get 'out of the dumps'.

II. Participants make collages from magazines or draw ways to get 'out of the dumps'. (Be sure to retrieve all snub-nosed scissors, glue and tape dispensers after group.) Participants share their work and receive peer feedback.

No Dumping

NEGATIVE THOUGHT

NEGATIVE THOUGHT

FACILITATOR'S INFORMATION
OVER THE HUMP

AGE	DIFFICULTY	PAGES
ALL	1	1

PURPOSE

See the whole picture versus making a 'mountain out of a molehill'.

MATERIALS

Board, marker, stuffed animal or picture of a bird, gummy candy worms, scotch tape, paper, pencils and crayons.

ATTENTION GRABBER

Volunteer draws the ground with a small hill on board. Someone adds grass and flowers, fruit and/or vegetables on right side of the hill. Someone tapes the gummy worm to the ground to the left of the molehill. Someone tapes the bird in the sky.

ACTIVITY

Ask:
1. How does the hill look to the worm? (Big)
2. What doesn't the worm see? (The fruit, vegetables, flowers on the other side)
3. What are the two things the worm sees? (Dirt or ground and big obstacle)
4. What does the bird see that the worm doesn't see? (The other side of the hill with all the goodies)
5. How are we like the worm? (See only the obstacles and they look insurmountable)
6. What's the value of the 'bird's eye view?' (See the mountain is really a molehill and see the rewards for overcoming the obstacles)
7. What do some worms do? (Give up)
8. What would the bird tell the worm to do? ("You can go over the hill; there are good things on the other side.")

Hand out crayons, paper and pencils.
They draw themselves in the worm's position and label their 'hill' (a current situation/obstacle). They then draw their goals on the other side and depict themselves 'over the hump' and reaping the benefits. Add to the drawings the steps they must take to get over the hump.

FOLLOW-UP

They share drawings with peers and each gets a cup of gummy worms as a reward.

Example:
'Hill' might be an upcoming test at school, a job interview or addiction.

Getting over the hump might include: study; preparing answers for anticipated interview questions and planning what to wear and how to get there; going to meetings, getting a sponsor, doing the 12 steps.

The 'rewards' or the other side can be drawn – passing the test, graduation; getting the job, money in the bank; being sober and all the benefits of health, relationships and peace of mind.

FACILITATOR'S INFORMATION
STINKING THINKING

AGE	DIFFICULTY	PAGES
ALL	1	2

PURPOSE

Identify and revise common negative thoughts.

MATERIALS

Board, marker, clipboards (2), pencils (2),
'STINKING THINKING' NEGATIVE THOUGHTS and/or STATEMENTS, page 49.
(Optional) prizes or play money (SKILLS BILLS, pages 277, 278).

ATTENTION GRABBER

Write STINKING THINKING on board and discuss its resultant negative feelings and actions.
Elicit examples of times an unpleasant thought led to negative feelings and actions:

I'm stupid
I'm ugly
I'll never make friends
I'll never get a good job
I'll never finish high school, college or vocational class
I'll never quit drinking, using and/or hurting myself
I've always had a bad temper
I can't compete with others
I'm always sick
I'm shy
People laugh at me
Suicide is an option
I'd like to kill _____

Tell them "We're going to change stinking thinking to positive but realistic thinking."

ACTIVITY

Teams separate and each develops a list. Use 'STINKING THINKING' NEGATIVE THOUGHTS AND/OR STATEMENTS, page 49. Volunteer keeps score on board. Teams reunite with chairs facing each other. First team reads negative statement. Opposing team members blurt out substitutions (positive but realistic relevant thoughts). They get one point per rebuttal. When they can think of no more, they read a statement and the other team rebuts. Continue until all negative thoughts have been rephrased. Team with the most points wins.

FOLLOW-UP

Each changes a current troublesome thought to a more positive realistic one.

VARIATION

Hand out play money to each player who rebuts a negative thought.
Team with the most money wins.

Stinking Thinking

NEGATIVE THOUGHTS and/or STATEMENTS

1.

2.

3.

4.

5.

6.

7.

8.

9.

10.

11.

12.

FACILITATOR'S INFORMATION
TFA

AGE	DIFFICULTY	PAGES
ALL	1	2

PURPOSE

Acknowledge that thoughts affect feelings and actions and importance of positive but realistic thoughts.

MATERIALS

Board, marker, pencils and 'TFA' WORKSHEET, page 51.

ATTENTION GRABBER

Volunteer draws a car and places an 'X' on driver's seat.
Ask, "Who is in the driver's seat – your thoughts or feelings?"
After debate, elicit and inform group that thoughts affect feelings and actions, and thoughts should be in the driver's seat.

ACTIVITY

Place on board (to represent Thoughts/Feelings/Actions)
'T'
'F'
'A'
Someone writes a negative thought and asks group to guess resultant feelings and actions.
Example: THOUGHT   I'm no good
              FEELING   Depression
              ACTION   Hurt self or drink alcohol
Next to the negative T, F, A, write another T, F, A, and ask group to change the initial negative thought to a positive but realistic one. Then members state the more positive feelings and actions that would follow.
Example: T: I'm worth something
               F: Hopeful
               A: Take care of grooming and health, take meds, go to therapy, enroll in school, attempt volunteer or paid job.

On the board, do a few examples with negative, then positive TFA.

Example: Negative   Positive
                T: T:
                F: F:
                A: A:

FOLLOW-UP

Each writes his/her most troublesome negative thought(s) on worksheet (same manner as board example) and changes negative to positive TFA. They share their work and receive feedback and/or suggestions.

TFA

WORKSHEET

Negative (-) thought/feeling/action below: Positive (+) thought/feeling/action below:

T

F

A

T

F

A

Negative (-) thought/feeling/action below: Positive (+) thought/feeling/action below:

T

F

A

T

F

A

Negative (-) thought/feeling/action below: Positive (+) thought/feeling/action below:

T

F

A

T

F

A

UNTANGLE YOUR THINKING

AGE	DIFFICULTY	PAGES
A & T	2	2

PURPOSE

Practice changing distorted thinking.

MATERIALS

String, board, marker, and 'UNTANGLE YOUR THINKING' METHODS, page 53.

ATTENTION GRABBER

Pass around small piece of tangled string.
"This is your thinking and we're going to practice untangling it."
Elicit that negative self-talk is the 'tangled thinking'.
(Be sure to retrieve the string.)

ACTIVITY

Take turns reading the methods/examples.
Each takes a turn writing his/her own negative thought on board.
S/he sits in the 'spotlight seat', selects and uses applicable methods.
Peers make suggestions.

FOLLOW-UP

Each shares his/her favorite method and tells how it is working with a current 'tangled' thought.

52

UNTANGLE YOUR THINKING

METHODS to UNTANGLE THINKING

1. **Define the distortion:**
    A. **All or Nothing / Black and White / Polarized Thinking:** you think you're good or bad, smart or dumb, a winner or a loser. You need to see 'shades of gray' or 'the middle ground'. No one is 100% successful in everything. Everyone has assets and limitations.
    B. **Overgeneralization:** Because something seems negative, you assume everything will always go wrong. You got a failing grade and decide you'll never graduate. Someone breaks up with you and you decide you'll never have a satisfying relationship.
    C. **Filtering:** You focus on the rubbish (like coffee grounds) and ignore the positives (the flavorful brew). You get 2-A's, 2-B's and a D. Instead of praising yourself for the A's and B's, you torture yourself over the D.
    D. **Jumping to Conclusions:** You immediately assume the worst. You think you can read minds. People are whispering or laughing and you know it's about you. You think you're a fortuneteller. "I'll never get promoted."
    E. **Catastrophizing or Magnifying or Minimizing:** You decide a small setback is a major catastrophe. You were reprimanded at work and are sure you'll be fired. You magnify your faults or the potential pitfalls of a situation and minimize your assets/achievements. You magnify others' attributes and ignore your own.
    F. **Emotional Reasoning:** You allow feelings to guide your thoughts. You are depressed and decide life is hopeless. If your moods are governed by a chemical imbalance they are unpredictable and inaccurate.
    G. **Shoulds – Also known as 'Musts', 'Oughts', 'Shouldn'ts':** You pressure or chastise yourself and others. Who has authority to dictate someone's behavior? You set yourself up for failure or anger. Don't 'should' on yourself or others.
    H. **Labeling:** You call yourself and/or others names like 'incompetent', 'ignorant', 'crazy' or 'lazy'. Labels stick in your mind and cause you to give up on yourself, others, relationships and/or situations.
    I. **Personalization:** You take something personally that is marginally relevant to you. You're late to work two times. When a memo is distributed about tardiness, you believe it's meant for you alone (forgetting that numerous co-workers come late).
    J. **Blaming:** You blame others for your joy or unhappiness. "If only he'd ask me out I'd be happy", "It's all her fault I'm in a bad mood". What others say or do affects you only with your permission. Happiness is an 'inside job' contingent on your view of self and circumstances.

2. **Thought Substitution - With a positive but realistic thought:**
    Replace "I'm stupid" with "I'm knowledgeable about some things but need to learn more about others."
    Replace "I'm ugly" with "I have some attractive features such as… (hair, eyes, etc.)."

3. **Do a Reality Check:**
    Ask yourself and others the true facts. Using pencil and paper, make lists if necessary. If you lost a job or relationship, list the number of jobs and/or relationship you have had. Look at the quality of whatever you lost (perhaps it's a blessing it's gone). Look at pros and cons of current situation and new opportunities. Decide it's not really the end of the world.

4. **Talk to Yourself with Compassion:**
    Be gentle with yourself. Note your positive steps and reward your risk-taking. Perhaps you got a D or F but at least you took the class. You weren't selected for a job but you learned more about applications and interviews for the next time. Give yourself a 'pep talk'.

5. **Shades of Gray:**
    See yourself, others and situations on a continuum. You're neither perfect nor worthless. Most people aren't 100% friend or foe. Situations aren't necessarily terrific or terrible. Decide you're a human being who <u>usually</u> succeeds but <u>sometimes</u> makes mistakes. Realize your friend is loyal 90% of the time. Your job is <u>mostly</u> pleasant with <u>some</u> annoying aspects.

6. **Substitute Terms:**
    Avoid emotionally laden words such as 'devastating', 'horrible', 'heartbroken'. Use 'disappointing', 'unfortunate', 'hurtful' to put things in perspective.

7. **Worst Case Scenario:**
    Consider (but don't dwell on) the worst possible outcome. Decide how you'll survive – the thoughts and/or actions you'll take to accept and overcome the situation. If you lose a job or relationship, what changes will you make to get and keep a more appropriate one?

To learn more about cognitive changes, consult <u>Ten Days to Self-Esteem</u> by David D. Burns, MD, © 1993, William Morrow and Company Inc.

WHAT'S THE POINT?

AGE	DIFFICULTY	PAGES
A & T	2	2

PURPOSE

To practice thought changing and action planning.

MATERIALS

Board, marker, container for CUT-UPS,
and 'WHAT'S THE POINT' QUOTES CUT-UPS, page 55,
which are *Shoot for the Moon* excerpts, by Meiji Stewart, copyright 1996 by Meiji Stewart.
Reprinted by permission of Hazelden Foundation, Center City, MN.

ATTENTION GRABBER

Volunteer selects one, writes it on board and discusses.

ACTIVITY

Participants take turns reading, writing on board, interpreting and relating each statement to themselves. Encourage them to draw a relevant cartoon on board.

FOLLOW-UP

Each tells a new idea derived from today's activity.

VARIATIONS

1. Dyads go to the front of the group and ask each other to interpret/apply the statements.
2. Each selects a few and writes his/her interpretation and application, then shares verbally.
3. Photocopy all and discuss as a group.
4. Teams ask the opposing team to interpret and play money or points are accrued.

WHAT'S THE POINT

QUOTES

1 "Shoot for the moon. Even if you miss, you will land among the stars."

2 "Do the thing you fear, and the death of fear is certain."
Ralph Waldo Emerson

3 "When you get to the end of your rope, tie a knot, hang on, and swing."
Leo Buscaglia

4 "Genius is one percent inspiration, and ninety-nine percent perspiration."
Thomas Edison

5 "Don't despair, it's often the last key of the bunch that opens the door."

6 "Eighty percent of success is just showing up."
Woody Allen

7 "Everybody is a genius, just on different subjects."

8 "A journey of a thousand miles begins with the first step."
Lao-Tsu

9 "You can't hit a home run unless you step up to the plate."
Kathy Seligman

10 "Look at a stone cutter hammering away at his rock, perhaps a hundred times without as much as a crack showing in it. Yet at the hundred-and-first blow it will split in two, and I know it was not the last blow that did it, but all that had gone before."
Jacob A. Riis

11 "There are no shortcuts to any place worth going."
Beverly Sills

12 "The greatest discovery of my generation is that a human being can alter his life by altering his attitudes."
William James

13 "To try is to risk failure. But the risk must be taken, as the greatest hazard in life is to risk nothing. The person who risks nothing, does nothing, has nothing and is nothing."

14 "One may not reach the dawn save by the path of night."
Kahlil Gibran

15 "Failure is delay, but not defeat. It is a temporary detour, not a dead-end street."
William Arthur Ward

16 "I have not failed. I've discovered one thousand ways not to build a light bulb."
Thomas Edison

Shoot for the Moon excerpts, by Meiji Stewart, copyright 1996 by Meiji Stewart. Reprinted by permission of Hazelden Foundation, Center City, MN.

You Are What You Do

AGE	DIFFICULTY	PAGES
ALL	1	2

PURPOSE

Take action toward goals and change from negative to positive thoughts and moods.

MATERIALS

Board, marker, 'YOU ARE WHAT YOU DO' WORKSHEET, page 57.

ATTENTION GRABBER

Volunteer writes, "You are what you eat" on board. Discuss theory that our health relates to nutrition. Another volunteer writes, "You are what you do" on board and elicits peoples' interpretations. Write on board and discuss: "You get what you expect." Then write and discuss: "Change the doing to change the viewing of yourself." "Get your feet going in the right direction and your head, heart and butt will follow."

ACTIVITY

'Auctioneer' calls out, or lists on board, the choices (from examples below and from group members' requests). Choices incorporate attributes they can develop by taking specific actions. People write choices and list 3 actions on front. They take turns reading the goal and actions to group (sit in 'spotlight seat') and write peer suggestions on the back.

EXAMPLES:
(For auctioneer to call or write on board and to be copied onto worksheet.)

"I want to be <u>calm</u>."   "I want to be <u>happy</u>."
"I want to be <u>courageous</u>."   "I want to be <u>attractive</u>."
"I want to be <u>friendly</u>."   "I want to be <u>assertive</u>."
"I want to be <u>sober</u>."   "I want to be <u>decisive</u>."
"I want to be <u>cooperative</u>."   "I want to be <u>self-accepting</u>."
"I want to be <u>smart</u>."   "I want to be <u>energetic</u>."
"I want to be <u>physically fit</u>."   "I want to be <u>mentally healthy</u>."
"I want to be <u>a sensible risk taker</u>." "I want to be <u>confident</u>."
"I want to be <u>brave</u>."   "I want to be <u>diligent</u>."
"I want to be <u>tolerant</u>."   "I want to be <u>patient with myself and others</u>."

On each worksheet:
    I want to be_____.
    Act _____ by doing this.
        1.
        2.
        3.

Sample:
    I want to be more honest.
    Act honest by doing this:
        1. Admit a mistake I recently made.
        2. Share a truthful thought and feeling.
        3. Do not cheat on a test, in a game, or in a relationship.
Each person decides his or her 'want' and identifies three actions on front. He or she then receives peer suggestions and lists those on the back.

FOLLOW-UP

The next day or week, they return and share whether they took actions or which actions they took, how they met the goal, how their attitudes about themselves have changed.

You Are What You Do

I want to be _____.

Act _____ by doing this:

1.

2.

3.

I want to be _____.

Act _____ by doing this:

1.

2.

3.

I want to be _____.

Act _____ by doing this:

1.

2.

3.

FACILITATOR'S INFORMATION
ZAPPERS

AGE	DIFFICULTY	PAGES
ALL	1	2

PURPOSE
To practice changing negative to positive but realistic thoughts.

MATERIALS
Board, marker, TV remote control and 'ZAPPERS' CUT-UPS, page 59.
(Optional) prizes or play money (SKILLS BILLS, pages 277, 278).

ATTENTION GRABBER
Ask, "What is this?", while showing the remote control.

Discuss its purposes – to turn on or off and change channels.
Explain: "We will practice zapping – turning off negatives and switching to positives."

ACTIVITY
Two teams face each other. 'Game Show Host' reads a negative thought – first team refutes with positive but realistic thoughts (as many as possible). Their points are marked on board.
The other team refutes the next negative thought and accrues points. Alternate teams refute negative thoughts until all have been read. Team with the most points wins.

FOLLOW-UP
Each shares his/her recent negative thought and its positive but realistic replacement.

VARIATION
Participants write negative thoughts on slips of paper. Use these for the game.

ZAPPERS

1 My life is ruined because of the past.	**2** I'm poor.	**3** I'll always be like this.
4 Nobody loves me.	**5** I've wasted too many years.	**6** I'm alone in the world.
7 I have no friends and I don't know how to make friends.	**8** Why should I try? Nothing ever works.	**9** I deserve to die.
10 I'm lazy.	**11** I'm ugly.	**12** I'm stupid
13 I was born this way.	**14** I'm crazy.	**15** People think I'm incompetent.
16 It's all my fault that I have a mental illness.	**17** I have to fight when I'm mad.	**18** I hate myself.
19 My situation is hopeless.	**20** I'll never get along with my family.	**21** I drag people down.
22 I'll never succeed at anything.	**23** I'll always be locked up.	**24** I'm a failure because I get D's and F's.

COPING SKILLS

COPING SKILLS help handle emotions, symptoms of mental illness, substance abuse, self-harm impulses and other problems. Participants identify benefits of therapy and ways to alleviate symptoms including medication management and behavioral interventions.

ACTIVITY	PAGE NUMBERS	AGE	LEVEL OF DIFFICULTY	PAGES
Coping Skills Alphabet	63 - 64	ALL	1	2
Crossword Clues	65 - 66	ALL	2	2
Doctor – Doctor	67 - 71	ALL	2	5
Don't Gang Up On Me	72 - 76	A & T	2	5
Emotions Charade	77 - 78	ALL	1	2
Frog Parable	79 - 81	ALL	1	3
From a Jack to a King to an Ace	82	ALL	1	1
Medicine ABC's	83 - 87	A & T	2	5
Medicine Match-Up	88 - 98	A & T	2	11
Panel Discussion	99 - 100	A & T	2	2
Picture Game	101 - 102	ALL	1	2
Tic-Tac Cope	103 - 105	ALL	2	3
Tic-Tac-Medicine	106 - 108	ALL	2	3
Twenty-One	109 - 114	A & T	3	6
Who Wants To Be A Pillionaire?	115 - 120	A & T	3	6

LEGEND

AGES:
ALL = ALL ages, 8 or 9 through adults
YP = YOUNG PEOPLE, ages 8 or 9 through 17
T = TEENS, ages 13 through 17
A & T = ADULTS and TEENS, ages 13 and older
A = ADULTS, ages 18 and older
* = SPECIFIC PAGES expressly for this population.

LEVEL OF DIFFICULTY:
1 = EASIER - basic language; minimal reading and writing
2 = MODERATE - introduces new terminology; incorporates life experiences
3 = MORE DIFFICULT - requires some prior knowledge or introduction of new information; promotes peer teaching

PAGES: The total number of pages related to the activity, including FACILITATOR'S INFORMATION and all accompanying pages.

COPING SKILLS ALPHABET

AGE	DIFFICULTY	PAGES
ALL	1	2

PURPOSE Identify coping skills or concepts related to mental health, meds and sobriety.

MATERIALS Board, marker and 'COPING SKILLS ALPHABET' WORKSHEET, page 64.

ATTENTION GRABBER Volunteer prints the letters of alphabet on board, under each other in two rows.

A	N
B	O
C	P
D	Q
E	R
F	S
G	T
H	U
I	V
J	W
K	X
L	Y
M	Z

ACTIVITY Group members take turns selecting a letter and write meaningful word, (example A = Anger, T = Time-out or M = Medicine), and share its relevance to them.

Each person receives questions and/or suggestions from peers, then selects the next person to go to the board.

FOLLOW-UP Write letters on paper. Individuals, dyads or teams write words for each letter. Discuss their choices.

COPING SKILLS ALPHABET

WORKSHEET

A	N
B	O
C	P
D	Q
E	R
F	S
G	T
H	U
I	V
J	W
K	X
L	Y
M	Z

CROSSWORD CLUES

AGE	DIFFICULTY	PAGES
ALL	2	2

PURPOSE

To identify concepts and terminology.

MATERIALS

Board, marker, and 'CROSSWORD CLUES', page 66.
Place chairs facing each other (2 teams).
(Optional) prizes or play money (SKILLS BILLS, pages 277, 278).

ATTENTION GRABBER

Label columns and draw squares on board (example below).
Ask, "How do you do a crossword puzzle?"
Explain they will be given clues for whatever letter they select and get points for guessing the word.

ACTIVITY

'Game Show Host' sits at board and calls on alternate people or teams. If the first person (or second, third, etc. whose turn it is) does not know the answer, teammates may help. If they answer incorrectly, the opposite team has a chance to answer that question. A correct response warrants an 'X' in the box under the letter. Then the opposing team chooses a letter and answers the next question. Team members take turns marking on the board. See the example and questions on the next page. Use a different color marker for each team.

A WORDS	D WORDS	P WORDS	C WORDS	T WORDS	S WORDS	V WORDS

Whichever team earns more points wins (color code 'X' marks).

Example: Team #1 uses blue marker and team #2 uses red for their 'X'.

FOLLOW-UP

Each shares the most meaningful term s/he encountered during group.

VARIATION

Any letters or topics can be addressed by developing relevant questions.

CROSSWORD CLUES

(Please note that answers follow the "=" mark and participants must guess the word.)

A WORDS
1. Fighting, explosive = **aggressive**.
2. Medicine that helps with sadness and anger = **antidepressant**.
3. Standing up for yourself politely. Saying no when necessary = **assertive**.
4. Medicine that helps with voices and paranoia = **antipsychotic**.
5. Another word for nervous = **anxious**.

D WORDS
1. Saying you don't have a problem when you do. Lying to yourself and others = **denial**.
2. Another word for extreme, ongoing sadness = **depression**.
3. Illegal substances to alter mood – people use them to feel better and then feel worse when they wear off = **drugs**.
4. When you drink too much alcohol, you become _____ = **drunk**.
5. Mixing prescribed drugs with alcohol or illegal drugs is _____ (another word for unsafe) = **dangerous**.

P WORDS
1. Being a doormat; not defending yourself = **passive**.
2. A medical doctor who treats mental illness with medicine = **psychiatrist**.
3. A doctor who treats mental illness with therapy (talking) = **psychologist**.
4. People who believe in a Supreme Being do this _____ = **pray**.
5. An antidepressant (name brand) = **Paxil, Prozac**.

C WORDS
1. Type of skill used to handle anger or depression = **coping**.
2. Finding fault with someone or something = **criticize**.
3. Bravery. Facing challenges = **courage**.
4. Opposite of nervous = **calm**.
5. People often dislike it but it is part of life. When something is different = **change**.

T WORDS
1. A way to remove yourself from an upsetting situation = **time out**.
2. What you must do if you are in danger (being abused or feeling suicidal) = **tell or talk**.
3. These influence your moods and actions = **thoughts**.
4. To have faith in others – to believe what they say = **trust**.
5. Honesty – What you must tell even if you did something wrong = **truth**.

S WORDS
1. To push down or cover up your feelings = **stuff**.
2. Depression means you feel _____ = **sad**.
3. A chemical in the brain that makes you feel less depressed = **serotonin**.
4. Feeling good about ourselves and proud = **self-esteem**.
5. Highest level on Maslow's Hierarchy of Needs = **self-actualization**.

V WORDS
1. To picture success or a calm scene in your mind = **visualize**.
2. Whatever you place high importance on = **value**.
3. The opposite of defeat. Overcoming fear or a problem = **victory**.
4. If you are treated badly, you feel like a _____ = **victim**.
5. Listen to that still small _____ of reason or conscience = **voice**.

DOCTOR - DOCTOR

AGE	DIFFICULTY	PAGES
ALL	2	5

PURPOSE

Identify facts about medicine and minimize adverse effects.

MATERIALS

Stethoscope or white coat or mock name tag with 'M.D.', container for CUT-UPS, 'DOCTOR - DOCTOR' CUT-UPS, page 68, and 'DOCTOR - DOCTOR' REFERENCE GUIDE FOR MEDICATIONS, pages 69-71.

ATTENTION GRABBER

Ask "Who has played doctor?"

Explain with this version, people play patient and doctor by asking and answering questions.

ACTIVITY

They take turns being 'M.D.' and patient.

The patient asks question (from CUT-UPS) and doctor answers. If the 'doc' needs help, the 'audience' assists. M.D. and patient sit at front of group facing each other. The 'patient' should not reveal the answer (on CUT-UP slip) until 'doctor' and audience have attempted to answer the question. Use 'REFERENCE GUIDE FOR MEDICATIONS', pages 69-71, for further information.

FOLLOW-UP

Each tells a question s/he needs to ask his/her doctor. If someone has no unanswered question, s/he identifies one medicine fact s/he learned today.

© 2001 Wellness Reproductions and Publishing, Inc. 1-800 / 669-9208

DOCTOR - DOCTOR

1 Doctor - Doctor:
Q Will my medicine make me a zombie or control my mind?
A It will help you think more clearly and cope with dangerous impulses.

2 Doctor - Doctor:
Q **What is Depakote?**
A Mood Stabilizer, anticonvulsant

3 Doctor - Doctor:
Q I keep forgetting my bedtime medicine. What should I do?
A Put it near your toothbrush or alarm clock or pajamas.

4 Doctor - Doctor:
Q **What is Prozac?**
A antidepressant

5 Doctor - Doctor:
Q **What is Paxil?**
A antidepressant

6 Doctor - Doctor:
Q **What is a mood stabilizer?**
A Helps with mood swings — happy then sad or mad.

7 Doctor - Doctor:
Q I keep forgetting my morning medicine. What should I do?
A Put it near coffee cup or a breakfast table.

8 Doctor - Doctor:
Q Sometimes my arms or legs get stiff. What should be done?
A Congentin can be prescribed.

9 Doctor - Doctor:
Q My medicine upsets my stomach. What should I do?
A Take it with food.

10 Doctor - Doctor:
Q I'm getting headaches a lot. What should I do?
A Over-the-counter pain reliever may help.

11 Doctor - Doctor:
Q I have a rash from my medicine. What should I do?
A Doctor will probably stop the medicine and may send you to ER or prescribe Benadryl or other medicine.

12 Doctor - Doctor:
Q My eyes are blurry. What should I do?
A This may get better. Wait for a few months before getting new glasses.

13 Doctor - Doctor:
Q I've been constipated since I started my medicine. What can I do?
A Get more exercise, bulk, fluids.

14 Doctor - Doctor:
Q My heart is beating fast lately. What should I do?
A This may improve or doctor may order an Electrocardiogram.

15 Doctor - Doctor:
Q **What is a hallucination?**
A Seeing, hearing, feeling, smelling, tasting things that are not real.

16 Doctor - Doctor:
Q Why do I have to take pills?
A Chemical inbalance in brain.

17 Doctor - Doctor:
Q What happens if I drink or use street drugs with my medicine?
A Could die or effects of medicine will be intensified or counteracted.

18 Doctor - Doctor:
Q I've been getting sunburns when I'm out for a short time. What should I do?
A Wear protective clothing, sunscreen, sunglasses.

19 Doctor - Doctor:
Q **What is an antidepressant?**
A Works on sadness, may help with appetite and sleep.

20 Doctor - Doctor:
Q **What is paranoia?**
A Think people are against you or they are after you, talking about you.

21 Doctor - Doctor:
Q **What is an antipsychotic?**
A Helps with delusions, hallucinations, thought disorders.

22 Doctor - Doctor:
Q I feel dizzy when I get up from bed quickly. What should I do?
A Sit and dangle legs, then stand slowly.

23 Doctor - Doctor:
Q Sometimes my hands shake. What should I do?
A This may get better or another medicine may be prescribed to stop it.

24 Doctor - Doctor:
Q My mouth is dry from my medicine. What can I do?
A Use sugarless gum /candy and drink more fluids — moisturize lips.

25 Doctor - Doctor:
Q I've gained weight. What can I do?
A Use sensible diet and increase exercise.

26 Doctor - Doctor:
Q I'm sleepy all day. What can I do?
A Keep active. Do not drive or operate machinery. Doctor may change doses or give most or all of the medicine at bedtime or earlier in the evening.

27 Doctor - Doctor:
Q I feel better — when can I stop my medicine?
A You may need to remain on the medicine for at least 6-9 months, then it might be gradually decreased.

DOCTOR - DOCTOR

Types of Medications

Antipsychotics, also known as Major Tranquilizers or Neuroleptics:

Used for acute agitation, Bipolar Disorder, Psychosis, Severe Dyscontrol, Schizophrenia, Tourette's Disorder and other conditions.

Help with hallucinations, delusions, paranoia, apathy, flat affect, insomnia, isolation, rage, disorganized thoughts, and other symptoms.

Common names are Thorazine, Serentil, Prolixin, Trilafon, Stelazine, Haldol, Navane, Taractan, Orap, Loxitane, Moban, Clozaril, Risperdal, Zyprexa, and Seroquel.

Antidepressants:

Used for Bipolar Disorder (Depressed), Depression, Obsessive Compulsive Disorder, Panic and Schizoaffective Disorder.

Help with anergia (no energy), anhedonia (loss of pleasure), guilt, poor concentration, excessive or deficient appetite and/or sleep, psychomotor agitation and/or retardation.

Common names are Elavil, Endep, Asendin, Anafranil, Sinequan, Adapin, Tofranil, Surmontil, Norpramin, Pamelor, Vivactil, Nardil, Parnate, Wellbutrin, Ludiomil, Desyrel, Prozac, Paxil, Zoloft, Luvox, Effexor, Serzone, and stimulants including Dexedrine, Ritalin, Cylert and Adderall. Stimulants are potentially addictive and mostly used in children with ADHD.

Mood Stabilizers:

Used for Bipolar Disorder (Manic-Depressive), and Schizoaffective Disorder.

Help with manic symptoms: threatening behavior, euphoria, grandiosity, hypersexuality, irritability, distractibility, pressured speech, and decreased sleep. They also help with depressive symptoms including somatic complaints.

Common names are Lithium, Tegretol, Depakote, and Neurontin. Note that Lithium can easily go from the therapeutic to toxic range (over 1.5 mEq/L) and requires blood tests for Lithium level, thyroid and kidney function. At toxic levels, symptoms mimic drunkenness: stomach upset, dizziness, staggering, slurred speech, and progress to problems with vision, movement, cardiac function, coma, convulsions, kidney failure and possible death. With Tegretol and Depakote, blood level, complete blood count and liver function tests are required.

Antianxiety Agents:

Used for Anxiety, Bipolar and Panic Disorder, akathisia (restless and uncontrollable movements), abstinence and withdrawal syndromes, and drug induced or psychotic agitation.

Help with nervousness, panic, phobia, backache, "butterflies", headache, palpitations, stomach pain, urinary/bowel frequency.

Common names are Xanax, Librium, Klonopin, Valium, Ativan, Serax, Centrax, and Buspar. All except Buspar have addictive potential and should be used short-term until stress reduction coping skills are developed. They should not be stopped abruptly but gradually tapered under doctor's supervision. Alcohol intensifies the effects and this can be deadly. Avoid activities requiring alertness (such as driving or operating machinery).

Side Effects of Most Psychotropics Include: sedation, dry mouth, constipation, low blood pressure (dizziness when changing position quickly), rapid heart beat, weight gain, increased or decreased blood sugar, increased or decreased sex drive, menstrual irregularities, stomach upset, blood or liver disorders, blurry vision, urine retention, excessive perspiration, and some lower the threshold for seizures or cause insomnia.

Serious: Hypertensive Crisis – Often with MAO Inhibitors (antidepressants), Nardil, Parnate: induced by eating or drinking tyramine in alcohol, broad beans, aged cheese, smoked fish or meat, summer sausage, and many other foods. Symptoms include headache, stiff neck, sweating, nausea, vomiting and increased blood pressure requiring immediate medical care (ER), where they will probably receive Procardia, Regitine or Thorazine.

Serious: Serotonin Syndrome – usually associated with antidepressants. Symptoms are agitation, confusion, sweating, diarrhea, flushing, jerky movements, restlessness, increased blood pressure and muscle stiffness and can lead to death.

Side effects of Antipsychotics include Extrapyramidal Syndrome – akathisia (a need to move, restlessness); akinesia (Parkinsonism,) including tremors, rigidity; dystonia or acute rigid muscles (back may arch and eyes may roll upward); "rabbit syndrome" or rapid mouth movements; Tardive Dyskinesia-abnormal movements of mouth and face.

Anticholinergic medication may be prescribed to decrease these symptoms (except Tardive Dyskinesia): akathisia, dystonia and pseudoparkinsonism. Examples of anticholinergics include Symmetrel, Cogentin, Artane, Benadryl, and Akineton. Inderal is also used for movements or tremors.

Note – a very serious but rare adverse effect: Neuroleptic Malignant Syndrome – rigidity, tremors, breathing difficulty, muteness, altered consciousness, increased temperature, pulse and blood pressure. Requires discontinuation of antipsychotic meds, no anticholinergic meds, and treatment with bromocriptine and dantrolene.

Treatment for common side effects:

Blurred vision — if symptoms persist doctor may change medications or dosage; see an ophthalmologist

Constipation — increase fluids, bulk, and exercise

Dizziness - move slowly from lying to sitting to standing, increase fluid

Drowsiness — ask doctor about decreasing daytime and increasing nighttime dose; keep busy, but take periodic rests; avoid driving or activities requiring alertness

Dry mouth — fluids, sugarless candy and/or gum, saliva substitutes are available

Insomnia — ask doctor to change dose to early in day; sleep hygiene education; decrease caffeine

Rapid heart beat — avoid excessive caffeine, monitor pulse, tell M.D.

Sexual difficulties — doctor may change medication or dose or times or may prescribe Yohimbine, Neostigmine, Viagra or another medicine. Some doctors may approve a week-end holiday from the medicine.

Stomach upset — take medication with food

Weight gain — nutritious low-cal diet with exercise

To learn more about Psychotropic medications, consult:

Isaacs, Ann, Mental Health Nursing, Lippincott-Raven Publishers, Philadelphia, PA., 1996.

Lego, Suzanne, Psychiatric Nursing, A Comprehensive Reference 2nd ed., Lippincott-Raven Publishers, Philadelphia, PA., 1996.

Mosby's Nursing Drug Reference, Mosby, Inc., St. Louis, MO, 1999.

Rollant, Paulette D. and Denise B. Deppoliti, Mental Health Nursing, Mosby's Review Series, Mosby Yearbook, Inc., St. Louis, MO., 1996.

Salzman, Carl, Psychiatric Medications for Older Adults-The Concise Guide, The Guilford Press, New York, NY, 2001.

DON'T GANG UP ON ME

AGE	DIFFICULTY	PAGES
A & T	2	5

PURPOSE
To refute erroneous ideas about medications.

MATERIALS
Board, marker, container for CUT-UPS,
'DON'T GANG UP ON ME' CUT-UPS, pages 73, 74,
and ANSWER KEY, pages 75, 76.

ATTENTION GRABBER
Write, "Don't gang up on me" on the board and ask, "What does it mean to gang up on someone?" Explain we are allowed to 'gang up' to teach correct ideas about medicine.

ACTIVITY
Take turns sitting in 'spotlight seat' with others in semicircle. 'Victim' reads erroneous statement and the others (one at a time) try to talk him/her out of it.

(Use 'DON'T GANG UP ON ME' CUT-UPS, pages 73, 74, for the list of erroneous statements).

FOLLOW-UP
Participants tell which wrong ideas 'hit home' with them and how they have changed their minds about medication.

DON'T GANG UP ON ME

1 Marijuana mellows me out. It's better than medicine.

2 I don't need medicine.

3 My medicine is going to slow me down in sports and schoolwork.

4 If it gives me a headache or upset stomach, I'm quitting it.

5 I'd rather stay sick, then I don't have to go to work or school.

6 Everybody is against me. Pills won't make them stop following or spying on me or talking about me.

7 I'm willing to take the medicine but I just keep forgetting. It's not my fault.

8 If the voices would just stop talking, I'd be fine. No medicine will make them shut up.

9 Everybody and everything around me should change. Then I wouldn't need the medicine.

10 My medicine can't undo all the things that happened in the past, so why take it?

11 If a doctor prescribes something for nerves or pain, I won't get addicted to it.

12 People who need pills to cope with life are stupid. The idiots around me are the ones who need it.

13 Nobody else needs medicine. I don't want to be different. I can do it all on my own. How can a pill change me?

14 When I take it at bedtime, I can't get up in the morning. I'll have to stop the pills.

15 If I take the pills, I'm giving up control to the doctors or my family. I want to be my own boss.

16 If I get better, everyone will expect too much from me.

17 The pills won't make me richer or better looking, so why take them?

18 I'll only take the medicine if it will make all my problems go away.

19 I'm not taking it in summer because I get worse sunburns and the sun bothers my eyes.

20 No one will fall in love with me if they know I need medicine.

21 I'll have to take it forever.

22 It makes my heart beat faster. I'll have a heart attack.

23 If I take medicine, no one will hire me.

24 I like my rages. They mean I'm tough. Medicine will make me a wimp.

73

DON'T GANG UP ON ME

25 I've been off my meds for a week and feel fine. That proves I don't need them.	**26** I'm quitting my pills. I almost keeled over when I jumped up from bed to answer the phone.	**27** I've heard some meds can ruin your liver or kidneys. I'm not taking chances. Forget it!
28 I want to get on tranquilizers. They make me feel as good as a few beers.	**29** My pill is the size of a horse pill. I could choke on it.	**30** I don't want to give up drinking and if I take the medicine, I shouldn't drink. Partying is very important.
31 I really hurt the staff or my family if I pretend to swallow my pills. Then I spit them out. I like to 'put one over' on them.	**32** If I take the medicine, I can't drive.	**33** The medicine won't change my family, friends, school or work problems, so why take it?
34 Antidepressants are addictive. I don't want to be a pill freak.	**35** I won't have control over my thoughts or my life if I'm on medicine.	**36** I took it everyday for 2 weeks and I still don't feel better, so I'm giving up. Wouldn't you?
37 The medicine will make me a zombie.	**38** My friend's arms, legs, back, neck and jaw got stiff from a medicine and it scared me to death. What if it happens to me?	**39** The medicine could ruin my sex life.
40 The medicine could make me fat.	**41** I'm cured. I feel better so I'm quitting my medicine.	**42** My medicine works better if I have a few drinks with it.
43 People will think I'm crazy if I take medicine.	**44** Why do I have to get blood drawn when I take medicine?	**45** Drinking makes me feel better than my medicine does.
46 It makes me too tired. I'm stopping it on my own.	**47** I'm Bipolar and love the energy and excitement of my highs. Medicine ruins it.	**48** I like my voices. They keep me company.

74

DON'T GANG UP ON ME

1. The effects of marijuana are false and temporary. Poor concentration and amotivational syndrome interfere with developing true coping skills to be more 'mellow' such as stress reduction techniques.

2. You may benefit from medicine. If your doctor or therapist recommends it, why not give it a fair trial? Denial of an illness or chemical imbalance prohibits progress.

3. Sedating effects usually wear off as your body adjusts to the med. Ask your M.D. if most or all can be taken at bedtime.

4. These problems may resolve by taking over-the-counter pain reliever or taking food and/or milk with meds.

5. Avoiding responsibility is a secondary gain. Without treatment, school and/or work seemed overwhelming. Medication makes it easier to face challenges.

6. Paranoia and blaming others are symptoms that meds may help.

7. Find ways to remember. Put it next to your coffee cup or toothbrush.

8. Voices are decreased by meds. If one medicine doesn't help another will.

9. People and things may not change but your reactions can be more appropriate with the help of medicine.

10. It stabilizes chemical imbalance. You can then focus better on coping with the past and present challenges.

11. Narcotic analgesics and minor tranquilizers are highly addictive and for short-term use only.

12. Without a chemical imbalance, it's easier to cope with difficult people.

13. Many people do take meds. There's plenty to do 'on your own.' Medicine and supportive people can help.

14. Ask your M.D. if you can take it at dinnertime or a couple of hours before bed. Then the drowsiness will be gone by morning.

15. Medicine is not mind control. It does not rob free will. It makes you more capable of thinking clearly and managing your own emotions.

16. Develop your own realistic expectations of yourself.

17. With proper body chemistry, you're better able to focus on self-improvement.

18. Nothing makes all your problems go away, but meds can help you concentrate on problem-solving skills.

19. Use protective clothing, sunblock and sunglasses.

20. You will be more likely to develop healthy relationships when your symptoms don't dominate your life. The right person will accept you and your need for medicine.

21. You may not need it forever. Your M.D. may eventually taper the dosage. If it helps, why fight it? Compare yourself to a person who has diabetes who can lead a normal life as long as s/he takes insulin.

22. Rapid heartbeat usually subsides. Monitor pulse, tell M.D. and tests may be ordered or medicine may be changed.

23. Most interviewers won't ask. Some jobs such as driving or operating machinery do not allow sedating meds. Your M.D. may change the times, dosage or medicine to accommodate your work schedule

24. The adrenaline rush gives a false sense of power. Medicine helps you focus on developing conflict-resolution skills versus aggression.

DON'T GANG UP ON ME

25. You feel fine because the medicine is still in your system.

26. This is due to a sudden position change, which drops blood pressure. Sit up slowly, dangle your feet and stand when light-headedness ceases.

27. Liver, kidney, thyroid function and other blood tests will be ordered by your M.D.

28. These are addictive 'quick-fixes.' Learn stress reduction techniques (deep breathing, meditation, imagery, exercise, and progressive muscle relaxation).

29. Your M.D. may order liquid. Some pills can be cut or crushed but some should not. Read labels.

30. Alcohol may intensify or counteract effects. If drinking is this important, it is probably interfering with your mental health.

31. Medication is not about power struggles. You make the decision to help or hurt yourself.

32. You may be able to drive depending on your medicine, dose, times, and how it affects your alertness.

33. It will make you better able to cope with people and situations.

34. Antidepressants are not addictive. They do not create euphoria.

35. They do not exert mind control. They help you to control your own thoughts, feelings and actions.

36. It may take three to six weeks to reach its full therapeutic level.

37. It should not make you that sedated! Give yourself time to adjust. Tell your M.D. if it persists. Enjoy the relief from troublesome symptoms.

38. This is unlikely with the newer meds, but if it happens it is easily corrected with another medicine (often Cogentin).

39. If a medicine affects erections or orgasms, tell your M.D. The medicine, dose or times may be changed. Some doctors allow 'weekend holidays' from meds. Do not be embarrassed to talk to your M.D. who understands the importance of sexuality for mental and physical wellness.

40. Weight can be regulated through diet and exercise. If problems persist, ask your M.D. to switch to another med. There are several without this adverse effect.

41. Symptoms are usually controlled, not cured. People who quit when improved often eventually relapse.

42. Mixing alcohol or other legal or illegal drugs with your medicine can be harmful or deadly! Also, alcohol usually worsens thought and mood symptoms, especially when it 'wears off.' 'Crashing' from speed makes depression worse.

43. You're likely to act 'crazy' without it! People need not know you take meds. True friends would encourage you to take it.

44. Blood is tested to see whether some meds are within the therapeutic range. Other reasons include checking for adequate red and/or white cells; liver, kidney, and thyroid function or to ensure no adverse effects.

45. Drinking provides a false sense of euphoria or serenity. In a few hours you usually feel worse. The right medicine combined with coping skills and supportive people and environment improve your quality of life.

46. Fight lethargy by keeping busy with interesting and challenging activity and give your body time to adjust. If drowsiness persists, your M.D. may change the med, dose or times.

47. The manic highs have dangerous features. Agitation, grandiosity, promiscuity, extravagance and intrusiveness are a few. They're often followed by regrets and severe depression. You may forego some excitement for stability, safety, peace of mind and healthier relationships.

48. Voices are usually making negative comments and often command harm to self and/or others. Meds and stable body chemistry will enhance your readiness to develop interpersonal skills.

EMOTION CHARADES

AGE	DIFFICULTY	PAGES
ALL	1	2

PURPOSE

Disclose emotions and ways to cope.

MATERIALS

Container for CUT-UPS, 'EMOTION CHARADES' CUT-UPS, page 78.

ATTENTION GRABBER

Before group, ask volunteer to portray boredom (slump down in chair).
Ask "What do you think s/he is feeling?"
Discuss how body language and facial expression communicate our feelings.
Ask one person to review how to play charades. (We convey ideas without speaking or writing.)

ACTIVITY

First person selects CUT-UP and portrays the EMOTION*. Correct guesser tells the most recent time s/he felt that emotion, how s/he might have handled it more appropriately (if applicable). If guesser already had a turn, s/he selects a peer who has not had a turn.

FOLLOW-UP

Participants make collages selecting magazine pictures relevant to their emotions and 'show and tell' about selections.

*EMOTIONS easily portrayed:

 Silly
Sad
Mad

 Happy
Nervous
Shy

 Afraid
Suicidal
Homicidal

 Ashamed
Excited
Energetic

*EMOTIONS requiring peer assistance to portray:

Helpful (Hand a glass of water or blanket to someone.)

Helpless (Lie on floor and someone pretends to step on you.)

Left out (2 people have pantomime of a conversation and ignore the third person.)

EMOTION CHARADES

1 SILLY	**2** SAD	**3** MAD
4 HAPPY	**5** NERVOUS	**6** SHY
7 AFRAID	**8** SUICIDAL	**9** HOMICIDAL
10 ASHAMED	**11** HELPFUL	**12** HELPLESS
13 LEFT OUT	**14** EXCITED	**15** ENERGETIC

FROG PARABLE

AGE	DIFFICULTY	PAGES
ALL	1	3

PURPOSE

To identify problem-solving actions through dramatization of a parable (a short, simple story from which a moral lesson may be drawn).

MATERIALS

Three copies of 'FROG PARABLE', page 80, one for narrator and two 'frogs', cream and butter,
'FROG PARABLE' WORKSHEET, page 81.

ATTENTION GRABBER

One volunteer holds cream and another holds butter. Ask "How does cream turn into butter?" and elicit responses related to churning and movement.

ACTIVITY

'Narrator' reads while 'actors' (frogs) pantomime and speak their lines. After the 'parable performance,' distribute worksheet. They can work independently, then share own answers or work in dyads. (Partners record each other's answers, then sit in front of group and 'present' each other. "This is Jane. A time she did nothing and a problem got worse was . . .")

FOLLOW-UP

Numerous books have 1-2 page tales that illustrate important lessons such as <u>The Chicken Soup for the Soul</u> series by Jack Canfield, <u>Stories for the Heart</u>, compiled by Alice Gray. Develop questions about the main points of the story. With permission of the publisher, photocopy several copies of the story, color code each part with highlighter, have a few props, household objects or simple costumes. Two or three parts are better for small groups (we need an audience). Allow time for practice, then 'actors' perform and participants answer questions.

FROG PARABLE

FROG PARABLE:

(Three participants read and practice this for a few minutes before performing for audience.)

Narrator:

Once upon a time, two frogs fell into a bucket of cream.
(both fall down)

One frog says

"I saw no way out and drowned." *(lies on floor as if dead)*

The other frog says

"I thrashed around trying to stay afloat."
(makes swimming or water treading motions)

Narrator:

After a while, all the movement churned the cream into butter and this frog hopped out. *(hops out, smiles and breathes freely)*

FROG PARABLE

A time I did <u>nothing</u> about a problem and it got <u>worse</u>.

_____

A time I did <u>something</u> and things got <u>better</u>.

_____

A problem I have <u>now</u>.

_____

Four things I can <u>do</u> about it.

1._____

2._____

3._____

4._____

From the <u>Frog Story</u> I learned—

_____

_____

_____

_____

_____

FROM A JACK TO A KING TO AN ACE

AGE	DIFFICULTY	PAGES
ALL	1	1

PURPOSE

Identify coping concepts, skills and wisdom.

MATERIALS

Board, marker, paper, pencils, stapler or tape, from a deck of playing cards – face cards and aces.

ATTENTION GRABBER

Show the cards. Ask volunteers to write on board vertically:

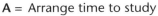

```
K          Q          J          A
I          U          A          C
N          E          C          E
G          E          K
           N
```

Use 'ACE' as an example and brainstorm ways to 'ACE' a test:

A = Arrange time to study
C = Check your answers
E = Exercise after studying to relieve stress

ACTIVITY

People work individually, in dyads or small groups.
Each selects a card, staples it to top of paper and writes its name and suit vertically on paper and thinks of relevant words.

Example for KING OF HEARTS:
K = Kind
I = Intelligent
N = Nice
G = Generous

O = Open to suggestions
F = Failure turned inside out is success

H = Higher Power
E = Energetic
A = Assertive
R = Recovery from the past
T = Think before you speak
S = Start now

The words and phrases need not relate to the stem-word (obviously we don't care about Kings, Queens, Jacks, Aces) but they should relate to mental health, recovery, spirituality or any pertinent topic.

Members share their work.

FOLLOW-UP

Each tells how s/he can move from a Jack to a King or Ace in one area of his/her life.

MEDICINE ABC's

AGE	DIFFICULTY	PAGES
A & T	2	5

PURPOSE
Identify medication concepts.

MATERIALS
Board, markers, 'MEDICINE ABC'S' LIST, page 84,
'MEDICINE ABC'S' SUGGESTED RESPONSES, pages 85-87,
(answer key with suggested responses but other correct answers may be accepted).

ATTENTION GRABBER
Volunteer writes alphabet (vertical) on board.
Explain: "Today we'll learn the ABC's of medicine."

ACTIVITY
Take turns writing a word next to the appropriate letter.
Explain the term. Ask peers for feedback.

FOLLOW-UP
Each shares a new concept acquired today.

VARIATION
Divide into teams. Opposing teams select letter and word for other team whose members must write on board and explain its meaning.

MEDICINE ABC's

A.	Antidepressant	Antipsychotic	Antianxiety
B.	Blurry	Brain chemicals	Benefits
C.	Constipation	Compulsion	Consequences
D.	Drugs	Drinking	Drowsy
E.	Effexor	Effects (side)	EEG
F.	Frequency	Fear	Food
G.	Grandiose	Grief	Group
H.	Hallucinations	Headache	Hungry
I.	Inhaler	Injection	Impulses
J.	Judgment	Jokes	Justification
K.	Knowledge	Keep (where?)	Kidney
L.	Lithium	Labels	Liver
M.	MAO Inhibitors	Mood stabilizer	Mania
N.	Nausea	Neurotransmitters	Nonverbal
O.	Orthostatic Hypotension	Obsession	Outcome
P.	Prozac & Paxil	Pregnancy	Potentiate
Q.	Questions	Quantity	Qualms
R.	Ritalin	Route	Risperdal
S.	Seroquel	Seizure	Substance abuse
T.	Tegretol	Tremors	Tardive dyskinesia
U.	Understanding	Urgent	Unusual
V.	Valproic acid	Vomiting	Valium
W.	Wellbutrin	Withdrawal	Word salad
X.	Xanax	X-ray	X – Sun is X-rated
Y.	Yellow	Young	Yesterday
Z.	Zyprexa	Zombie	Zero tolerance

(X – Sun is X-rated – some meds cause eyes & skin to be super-sensitive to sun)

MEDICINE ABC's

A. **Antidepressant** – treats sad mood
   Antipsychotic – treats thought disorder (paranoia, hallucinations, and delusions)
   Antianxiety – treats nervousness – can be addictive

B. **Blurry** – visual problems are side effects of some medicines
   If they don't improve tell M.D.
   Brain chemicals – some examples are dopamine and serotonin; an imbalance can cause thought and mood disorder; medicine helps balance them
   Benefits – good results; usually therapy and medication help improve symptoms

C. **Constipation** – a side effect of some meds; helped by increasing fluids, fiber, exercise
   Compulsion – feeling driven to do something (like handwashing or checking locks several times unnecessarily)
   Consequences – positive or negative but usually relate to unpleasant results
   Examples – threats and violence may lead to jail; street drugs and/or alcohol may harm physical and/or mental health

D. **Drugs** – may be prescribed or illegal, useful or harmful
   Drinking – may be harmful when taking most psychotropic meds
   Drowsy – side effect of many meds; avoid driving or other activities requiring alertness

E. **Effexor** – an antidepressant
   Effects (side) – unplanned effects from a medicine may be minor or serious
   Examples: dry mouth, dizziness, rapid heart beat
   EEG – Electroencephalogram – tests the electrical activity of brain; helps diagnose seizure disorder

F. **Frequency** – how often medicine is to be taken (once, twice, three or four times daily)
   Fear – may be due to scary voices or false beliefs; some people are afraid to ask for help or to take meds
   Food – helpful with many psychotropic meds which could upset stomach if taken without food or milk

G. **Grandiose** – People with Bipolar Disorder may have delusions that they are famous or extremely powerful and important
   Grief – A normal reaction to loss; helped by support groups and counseling
   Group – Type of therapy where people discuss feelings and issues and help each other; some groups are educational or for support

H. **Hallucinations** – Seeing, hearing, smelling, tasting, feeling, things that are not real
   Headache – May relate to stress or side effects; may be more serious
   Hungry – Getting too hungry may add to anxiety, anger, or worsen drug and/or alcohol cravings

I. **Inhaler** – Used by people with asthma or other respiratory problems; should be used as directed as it is medication
   Injection – A 'shot' for quick results from medication
   Impulses – Often quick response to anger or sadness; often lead to harming self or others and need to be controlled; meds and coping skills help

MEDICINE ABC'S

J. **Judgement** – adequate decision-making; may be poor if under the influence of street drugs and/or alcohol or if thoughts and/or moods are distorted

   Jokes –Often helpful to avoid taking self and/or situations too seriously but sometimes used to cover uncomfortable feelings or embarrassment

   Justification – reasons for needing therapy and/or medication

K. **Knowledge** – "Is Power" – helps people make decisions about meds, therapy, relationships, lifestyle

   Keep – keep meds in cool, dark, dry location and out of reach of children; check expiration dates

   Kidneys – help eliminate wastes; blood test for kidney function required with some meds

L. **Lithium** – a mood stabilizer

   Labels – to be read and followed; ask MD or pharmacist if unsure

   Liver – helps eliminate wastes. Blood tests for liver function required with some meds. Alcohol and street drugs harm the liver and other organs

M. **MAO Inhibitors** – antidepressant medicine with many dietary restrictions and drug interactions

   Mood stabilizer – helps with Bipolar Disorder, with extreme highs and lows
   Examples: Lithium, Depakote, Neurontin, and Tegretol.

   Mania – mood wherein people may be unusually excited, energetic, agitated; may overwork, overspend, be sexually promiscuous

N. **Nausea** – a side effect of some meds; taking medicine with food or milk often helps

   Neurotransmitters – brain chemicals related to our thoughts, moods, alertness, and anxiety

   Nonverbal – clues to a person's thoughts and feelings including facial expression and body position
   Example – red face and clenched fists signify anger.

O. **Orthostatic hypotension** – some meds cause lightheaded feelings and a drop in blood pressure with quick position changes; move slowly from lying to sitting to standing to avoid this

   Obsession – a recurring bothersome thought; interferes with daily activities; might command us to count, check, and perform unnecessary behaviors repeatedly

   Outcome – the end result; positive or negative.
   Example – the desired outcomes of a med and/or therapy may be improved mood and safer behavior

P. **Prozac & Paxil** – examples of antidepressants

   Pregnancy – notify your psychiatrist immediately; many meds are unsafe for the baby

   Potentiate – to make a medicine more powerful; this can be dangerous
   Example – alcohol may potentiate the effects of tranquilizers and can slow down heart and/or breathing and lower blood pressure to point of coma or death

Q. **Questions** – should be asked about purpose and side effects of meds

   Quantity – the amount or number dispensed (usually one month's supply);
   read label to see number of pills to take at one time;
   Example – "take 2 pills each day before breakfast and 3 pills at bedtime"

   Qualms – uneasiness and/or doubts, often about meds; talk about them instead of avoiding meds. Some people have qualms about disclosing personal information but need to share with a trusted professional.

MEDICINE ABC's

R. **Ritalin** – given usually to children with Attention Deficit Hyperactivity Disorder
   Route – the way a medicine gets into the body (through mouth, nasal inhalation, and injection)
   Risperdal – an antipsychotic med; helps with voices and/or paranoia and other symptoms of thought disorder

S. **Seroquel** – an antipsychotic med; helps with voices and/or paranoia and other symptoms of thought disorder
   Seizure – sudden brief change in level of consciousness, motor function, and sensory perception; some medicines that help seizures also help Bipolar Disorder (Depakote, Tegretol, Neurontin).
   Substance abuse – using street drugs or alcohol usually worsens thought and/or mood disorders and substances usually interact dangerously with prescribed meds

T. **Tegretol** – a mood stabilizer and anticonvulsant
   Tremors – quivering and/or involuntary movements of the hand or other body parts; sometimes a side effect of medication
   Tardive dyskinesia – involuntary movements of the face, jaw, tongue, lip smacking, drooling; sometimes occurred after long term treatment with the older antipsychotic meds

U. **Understanding** – knowing about symptoms, treatment and support groups
   Urgent – immediate help required for suicidal and/or homicidal plans, as we cannot wait for medication effects (could take weeks); an allergic reaction (rash, respiratory distress) requires emergency care
   Unusual – an unexpected reaction to a medication

V. **Valproic acid** – a mood stabilizer; Depakote/Depakene
   Vomiting – may be a side effect or symptom of serious drug toxicity; tell M.D. if it persists.
   Valium – an antianxiety med; can be very addictive

W. **Wellbutrin** – example of an antidepressant
   Withdrawal – unpleasant and potentially dangerous symptoms when certain prescribed or illegal drugs and/or alcohol are stopped. Some medicines can make withdrawal safer and more comfortable. Some medicines (like tranquilizers) should not be abruptly stopped but gradually tapered under M.D.'s supervision.
   Word salad – words with no sensible attachment or relevance; a symptom of schizophrenia and/or disorganized thinking

X. **Xanax** – an antianxiety med which can be habit-forming
   X-ray – helps diagnose physical abnormalities but psychiatric disorders are more difficult to diagnose and require honest communication with therapist and psychiatrist
   X-rated Sun – eyes and skin may be overly sensitive; use sunglasses, sunscreen, hats, protective clothing

Y. **Yellow** – if eyes and/or skin appear yellow, tell MD immediately
   Young – younger people and the elderly are more sensitive to most medications
   Yesterday – we can learn from past experiences; avoid dwelling on regrets

Z. **Zyprexa** – newer antipsychotic med.
   Zombie – over sedation; may improve or M.D. will change dose of med.
   Zero tolerance – for suicide, homicide, violence and/or substance abuse

MEDICINE MATCH-UP

AGE	DIFFICULTY	PAGES
A & T	2	11

PURPOSE

Identify medicines, purposes, ways to minimize side effects and pertinent information.

MATERIALS

Board, marker, 'MEDICINE MATCH-UP' MEDICATION INFORMATION SHEETS, pages 89 - 97, to be photocopied, cut on the designated lines, and distributed to group members, depending on which medications they take, 'MEDICINE MATCH-UP' WORKSHEET, page 98.

ATTENTION GRABBER

List participants' names on left and medicines on right (include medicines taken by all participants but in random order). Explain: Each draws a line from own name to his/her medicine(s) on board.

ACTIVITY

Distribute MEDICATION INFORMATION SHEETS, pages 89 - 97, relevant to each person's medication(s) and WORKSHEET, page 98. Allow time for writing answers. Each discusses his/her medications, stating their purpose, potential adverse effects, ways to minimize side effects, interactions with foods and/or medicines, required labs and other precautions (either from memory or s/he uses the medication information sheets and worksheet). Peers provide assistance.

FOLLOW-UP

Discuss physiological and environmental causes and treatments regarding emotional problems. Use stick figure and write 'internal factors' above figure, as noted in the diagram. Label 'chemical imbalance' and 'inherited traits'. Then brainstorm external factors – surround stick figure with 'family problems', 'abuse', 'grief and/or loss', 'drugs and/or alcohol' and others.

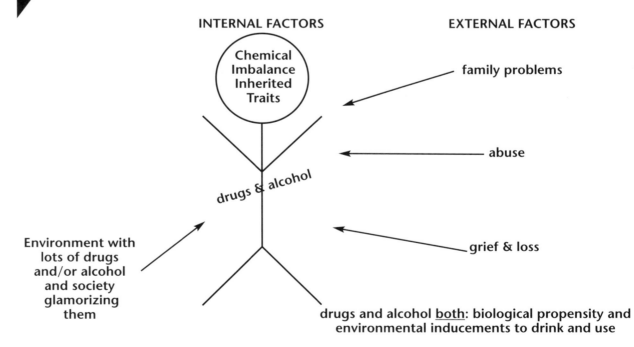

INTERNAL FACTORS   EXTERNAL FACTORS

Chemical Imbalance Inherited Traits

family problems

abuse

drugs & alcohol

grief & loss

Environment with lots of drugs and/or alcohol and society glamorizing them

drugs and alcohol <u>both</u>: biological propensity and environmental inducements to drink and use

Discuss value of medications primarily for internal factors and therapy primarily for environmental stressors. Ask, "Which treatment is better?" Elicit conclusion that both are essential for recovery.

MEDICINE MATCH-UP

SSRIs (Selective Serotonin Reuptake Inhibitors):

PROZAC / fluoxetine   PAXIL / paroxetine   ZOLOFT / sertraline

LUVOX / fluvoxamine   CELEXA / citalopram

Miscellaneous Antidepressants:

WELLBUTRIN / buproprion   DESYREL / trazodone   SERZONE / nefazodone

EFFEXOR / venlafaxine   REMERON / mirtazapine

ANTIDEPRESSANTS treat these symptoms: low energy, loss of pleasure, changes in appetite and/or sleep, concentration problems, preoccupation with guilt or death, hopelessness and helplessness.

SIDE EFFECTS: Consult your doctor and pharmacist for specific information. Medicines in this category may have some of these side effects and considerations plus others not mentioned here.

DRY MOUTH: Chew sugarless gum or candy, increase fluids, ask doctor about artificial saliva

BLURRED VISION: Avoid driving or operating machinery or other activities requiring clear vision until problem subsides and consult an ophthalmologist; may improve in one to two weeks

CONSTIPATION: Increase fluids, fiber, exercise

DIZZINESS: Change positions slowly, have blood pressure checked

DROWSINESS OR WAKEFULNESS MAY OCCUR: If the medicine makes you sleepy, avoid activities requiring alertness and ask your doctor if you can take it at night. If it keeps you awake, ask doctor to prescribe it for morning.

SUN SENSITIVITY: Wear protective clothes, sunscreen, sunglasses

HEADACHE OR BACK PAIN: Check with your doctor about over-the-counter medicines

RAPID HEART BEAT, PALPITATIONS OR CHEST PAIN: Monitor pulse and check with your doctor

CHANGES IN SEXUAL FUNCTIONING: Tell doctor who may change the medicine or prescribe a medicine to help this problem

CONSIDERATIONS: Discuss with doctor your medical history, intentions to become pregnant or to breastfeed, any prescribed medicines you recently took or are currently taking, and any alcohol, drugs and / or over-the-counter medications you use or recently took. Do not use with MAO INHIBITORS (a type of antidepressant) or with tryptophan. Report any unusual symptoms and / or reactions immediately (excessive sweating, muscle twitches, spasms, stiffness, flushing, fever, rash, respiratory problems or others).

MEDICINE MATCH-UP

ELAVIL / amitriptyline
ANAFRANIL / clomipramine
VIVACTIL / protriptyline

SINEQUAN or ADAPIN / doxepin
NORPRAMIN / desipramine
ASENDIN / amoxapine

TOFRANIL / imipramine
PAMELOR / nortriptyline
SURMONTIL / trimipramine

TRICYCLIC ANTIDEPRESSANTS treat these symptoms: low energy, loss of pleasure, changes in appetite and sleep, concentration problems, preoccupation with guilt or death, hopelessness and helplessness

SIDE EFFECTS: Consult your doctor and pharmacist for specific information. Medications in this category may have some of these side effects and considerations plus others not mentioned here.

DRY MOUTH: Drink fluids, use sugarless gum or lozenges, ask doctor about artificial saliva

CONSTIPATION: High fiber foods, increase fluids, exercise, ask doctor about stool softeners

BLURRED VISION: Avoid activities requiring clear vision for safety, consult an ophthalmologist. The problem may stabilize after a few weeks

RAPID HEART BEAT: Discuss with doctor, an electrocardiogram may be ordered before you start the medicine, tell doctor about any history of heart problems

DIFFICULTY URINATING: Drink adequate fluids, inform doctor

INSOMNIA: Ask doctor about taking the medicine in the morning

DIZZINESS, ESPECIALLY WHEN SWITCHING FROM LYING DOWN TO SITTING AND/OR STANDING: Have your blood pressure checked in these positions, change positions slowly (sit on bed and dangle feet before standing)

NERVOUSNESS AND/OR TREMORS: May resolve but tell doctor if they persist

DROWSINESS: Use caution operating equipment and driving or with other activities requiring alertness, ask doctor about bedtime doses

CONSIDERATIONS: Tell doctor if you have seizure disorder, rapid cycling bipolar disorder, narrow angle glaucoma, heart or prostate problems or other medical conditions. Inform doctor if you are or intend to become pregnant or breastfeed. Disclose full medical history including use of alcohol, drugs and/or over the counter and prescribed medicine you recently took or currently use. Do not use with MAOI(Monoamine Oxidase Inhibitors-a type of antidepressant). Report any unusual symptoms and/or reactions immediately.

NARDIL / phenelzine   PARNATE / tranylcypromine

ANTIDEPRESSANTS-MAOIs (MONOAMINE OXIDASE INHIBITORS) treat these symptoms:
low energy, loss of pleasure, changes in appetite and sleep, concentration problems, preoccupation
with guilt or death, hopelessness and helplessness

SIDE EFFECTS: Consult your doctor or pharmacist for specific information.
Medicines in this category may have some of these side effects and considerations plus others not
mentioned here.

    ANTICHOLINERGIC:
        DRY MOUTH - Use fluids, sugarless gum and/or candy, possibly artificial saliva, and moisturize lips.
        BLURRED VISION - Avoid driving and other activities requiring visual acuity until this subsides,
        consult an ophthalmologist.
        URINE RETENTION AND CONSTIPATION- Increase fluid, fiber, exercise and notify doctor if
        these persist.

    CARDIOVASCULAR:
        DIZZINESS OR LIGHTHEADEDNESS - Change positions slowly, have your blood pressure
        checked in lying, sitting and standing positions.
        RAPID OR IRREGULAR HEARTBEAT - Inform your doctor, an electrocardiogram may be
        ordered, monitor your pulse

SEDATION: Avoid driving and other activities requiring alertness, ask doctor about taking
medicine at bedtime instead of morning. Keep busy and active to counteract drowsiness.

RESTLESSNESS: INSOMNIA and ANXIETY-Ask doctor if you can take full dose in the morning to
prevent interference with sleep. Use relaxation techniques and sleep hygiene (quiet activities
before bed, limit daytime naps, avoid caffeine late in the day, etc.).

OTHERS: SUN-SENSITIVITY - Use protective clothing, sunscreen and sunglasses.
        DIARRHEA, ABDOMINAL PAIN, HEADACHE - If they occur may be treated by your doctor.
        MUSCLE TWITCHES AND/OR TREMORS, CHANGES IN APPETITE OR WEIGHT OR SEXUAL
            FUNCTION - Should be reported to your doctor.

HYPERTENSIVE CRISIS: SERIOUS BUT PREVENTABLE! Tyramine-containing foods and many
prescribed and over-the counter medicines must be avoided approximately two weeks before, during
and two weeks after treatment with MAOI medications. Symptoms include: headache, nausea,
vomiting, pallor, chills, stiff neck, muscle twitching, palpitations, chest pain, sweating and severe
high blood pressure. This is a medical emergency and you must go to an Emergency Room immediately.
**Prevent Hypertensive Crisis by following these guidelines, reading pharmacy information and
discussing medical history, diet, alcohol, drugs, other medications, pregnancy or breastfeeding
plans with doctor and dentist. Certain medical conditions and surgery anesthetics prohibit use
of MAOI Medications.**

MEDICINE MATCH-UP

<u>**Avoid foods with tyramine including**</u>: cheese, especially aged and / or aromatic cheeses and cheddar, parmesan, mozzarella; protein fermented or aged; beer, red wine or sherry, chianti; liquors, cognac; yeast or protein extracts; fava or broad beans or pods; beef or chicken liver; spoiled or over-ripe fruit; bananas and their peel; yogurt; brewer's yeast; pickles; sauerkraut; figs; raisins; pickled herring, salmon or pate; smoked salmon (lox); snails; chocolate; licorice; soy sauce; coffee and / or tea; meat extracts or smoked meats; pickled meats; sour cream, avocado, New Zealand spinach, clear spirits and white wine should be limited also. Please note that some sources indicate some of the foods and / or beverages may be used in moderation. Please check with your doctor and pharmacist for a specific list of foods and / or beverages to avoid and ask which (if any) may be consumed in limited amounts. Please be sure you know what amounts are considered 'limited' or 'moderate'. **Consulting a dietitian is highly recommended!**

<u>**Avoid over-the-counter medications**</u> for colds, allergies, congestion and coughs; narcotics; inhalants for asthma; local anesthetics with epinephrine; weight reducing pills and possibly other medications (read labels carefully). **The importance of discussing all medications with MD and pharmacist is emphasized!**

<u>**Prescribed medications with potentially dangerous or fatal interactions with MAOIs include but are not limited to**</u>: tricyclic antidepressants, narcotics, some blood pressure medications, sedatives, general anesthetics, DEMEROL/meperidine, stimulants, some diuretics, and several other medications which must be avoided with MAOI Medications. Be aware: Medications for diabetes including insulin and oral agents may cause hypoglycemia (seriously low blood sugar) when taking MAOI Medications. Alcohol, barbiturates, sedatives and tranquilizers should be avoided or used in reduced doses. **The importance of discussing all medications with M.D. and pharmacist is emphasized!**

ESKALITH/lithium   LITHOBID/lithium
Anticonvulsants used to treat mood disorders include:
TEGRETOL/carbamazepine   DEPAKOTE or DEPAKENE/Valproic Acid
NEURONTIN/gabapentin   LAMICTAL/lamotrigine

MOOD STABILIZERS: used for Bipolar Disorder treat these symptoms: 1. mania including assaultive or threatening behavior, distractibility, grandiosity, hypersexuality, delusions, decreased sleep, pressured speech; 2. depression including guilt, hopelessness, sadness, appetite and sleep problems.

Consult your doctor and pharmacist for specific information. These medications may have some of the side effects and considerations listed below and possibly others.

lithium (a naturally occurring salt)

SIDE EFFECTS MAY INCLUDE: fine hand tremors, weight gain, excessive urination, upset stomach, cramps, tiredness. It may contribute to underactive thyroid and mild diabetes. Blood tests, including thyroid and kidney function should be done before and during treatment. Some people experience a metallic taste in their mouths. Blood levels are monitored to adjust dosage as there is a narrow range between therapeutic and toxic levels. Adequate salt and fluids are essential.

Mild toxicity symptoms include low energy, poor concentration, slight staggering, muscle weakness, coarse hand tremors, slight muscle twitching and stomach upsets. Moderate toxicity symptoms include worse tremors and/or twitching; severe nausea, vomiting and diarrhea; worse staggering and poor coordination; slurred speech; dizziness; sedation and confusion; ringing in the ears and blurred vision. Severe toxicity involves involuntary eye movements, muscle contractions, visual or tactile hallucinations, fever, decreased blood pressure, electrocardiogram changes, decreased or no urination, seizure, stupor, coma, and death.

To decrease side effects
STOMACH UPSET: Take with food or milk
TREMORS: Restrict caffeine and ask doctor about INDERAL/propranolol
THIRST: Drink at least eight glasses of water daily
WEIGHT GAIN: Do not restrict water or salt; healthy foods and exercise (ask M.D., Dietician)
MUSCLE WEAKNESS, FATIGUE: Alternate periods of rest and activity, avoid driving and activities requiring alertness when drowsy, do not smoke alone or in bed
HAIR LOSS: M.D. will assess thyroid function
MORE FREQUENT URINATION: To be expected as thirst and fluids are increased

CONSIDERATIONS: Be sure to replace fluids and/or electrolytes lost through vomiting and/or diarrhea, exercise, perspiration, heat exposure. Many medications interact dangerously with lithium including some antipsychotics, antidepressants, diuretics, antibiotics, nonsteroidal anti-inflammatory drugs, muscle relaxants and anesthetics. M.D. should be monitoring lithium blood levels, blood cell counts, kidney, thyroid and cardiac function. Discuss with M.D. your medical history and/or problems, over-the-counter and prescribed medications you recently took or currently take, any alcohol and/or drug use, any plans for pregnancy or breastfeeding (usually not advisable). Carry an ID card stating you take lithium. Call M.D. if you have any of these symptoms: vomiting, diarrhea, hand tremors, muscle weakness, ringing in the ears or other side effects.

93

TEGRETOL / carbamazepine

ANTICONVULSANTS USED TO TREAT MOOD DISORDERS: treat these symptoms: mania including assaultive and threatening behavior, distractibility, grandiosity, hypersexuality, delusions, decreased sleep, pressured speech; depression including guilt, hopelessness, sadness, appetite and sleep problems. Consult M.D. and pharmacist for specifics. Medicines in this category may have some of these side effects and considerations plus others not mentioned. Inform M.D. of any persistent or troublesome effects.

SIDE EFFECTS:

DIZZINESS, DROWSINESS, VISUAL PROBLEMS: Avoid activities requiring alertness and good vision (driving and machinery operation) until these stabilize. Get routine eye exams. Change positions slowly. Irritability may occur.

HEART AND/OR BLOOD PRESSURE PROBLEMS: Have heart and blood pressure monitored by M.D.

STOMACH UPSETS: Take with food.

RESPIRATORY SYMPTOMS, SORE THROAT, FEVER, CHILLS: Tell M.D.

DRY MOUTH, DECREASED URINATION: Increase fluids, use sugarless gum and candy, ask about saliva substitute. Urinate before each dose.

RASHES, ITCHING, SUN SENSITIVITY: Tell M.D., use sun screen, sunglasses, protective clothing.

Discuss with M.D. medical history and problems, prescribed and over-the-counter medicines or drugs and/or alcohol used recently and/or currently and any plans for pregnancy or breastfeeding. Do not use with MAOIs (Nardil or Parnate). Report any unusual symptoms and/or side effects to your doctor. Complete blood count, liver and kidney function blood tests and Tegretol levels should be checked.

DEPAKOTE / DEPAKENE / Valproic Acid

ANTICONVULSANTS USED TO TREAT MOOD DISORDERS: treat these symptoms:
mania including assaultive and threatening behavior, distractibility, grandiosity, hypersexuality, delusions, decreased sleep, pressured speech; depression including guilt, hopelessness, sadness, appetite and sleep problems. Consult M.D. and pharmacist for specifics. Medicines in this category may have some of these side effects and considerations plus others not mentioned. Inform M.D. of any persistent or troublesome effects.

SIDE EFFECTS MAY INCLUDE BUT ARE NOT LIMITED TO:

DIZZINESS, DROWSINESS, HEADACHE, VISUAL PROBLEMS - Avoid activities requiring good vision or alertness, (driving and machine operation) until these subside. Change positions slowly, get eye exam. Ask doctor about bedtime dosing and pain relievers for headache.

STOMACH UPSETS, CHANGE IN APPETITE, CONSTIPATION OR DIARRHEA- Take with food and never crush or chew the tablets. Liquid form is available. For constipation, increase fluids, fiber and exercise. For diarrhea, replace fluids and tell M.D.

SKIN RASHES OR CHANGES IN HAIR GROWTH - Tell M.D.

Blood counts, Valproic Acid levels and liver function blood tests are done. Tell M.D. about medical history and problems, recent and / or current use of alcohol or drugs, prescribed and / or over-the-counter medicine, any plans for pregnancy or breast-feeding. Report any unusual symptoms and / or side effects to M.D.

- -

ANTICONVULSANTS USED TO TREAT MOOD DISORDERS: treat these symptoms:
mania including assaultive and threatening behavior, distractibility, grandiosity, hypersexuality, delusions, decreased sleep, pressured speech; depression including guilt, hopelessness, sadness, appetite and sleep problems. Consult M.D. and pharmacist for specifics. Medicines in this category may have some of these side effects and considerations plus others not mentioned. Inform M.D. of any persistent or troublesome effects.

NEURONTIN / gabapentin is a relatively new anticonvulsant, sometimes used for mood disorders, usually in combination with other mood stabilizers or antidepressants. The main side effect is drowsiness. Ask M.D. about bedtime dosing and avoid activities requiring alertness (driving or machinery operation). Do not smoke alone or in bed. Consult doctor and pharmacist for specifics.

LAMICTAL / lamotrigine is a relatively new anticonvulsant, used sometimes for mood disorders. It could cause a rash which should be reported to M.D. Consult doctor and pharmacist for specifics.

MEDICINE MATCH-UP

THORAZINE / chlorpromazine
PROLIXIN / fluphenazine
NAVANE / thiothixene
MOBAN / molindone
ZYPREXA / olanzapine

HALDOL / haloperidol
TRILAFON / perphenazine
LOXITANE / loxipine
CLOZARIL / clozapine
SEROQUEL / quetiapine

SERENTIL / mesoridazine
STELAZINE / trifluoperazine
ORAP / pimozide
RISPERDAL / risperidone

ANTIPSYCHOTIC MEDICATIONS treat these symptoms: hallucinations, delusions, disorganized thinking, paranoia, lack of motivation or energy and impaired social interaction.

SIDE EFFECTS: Consult your doctor and pharmacist for specifics. Medications in this category may have some of these side effects and considerations plus others not mentioned. Tell your doctor about any troublesome and / or persistent effects

EPS - EXTRAPYRAMIDAL SYMPTOMS: Most of these can be treated with anticholinergic or other medications including Artane, Cogentin, Benadryl, Akineton, Kemidren, Symmetrel, Parlodel, Inderal. Sometimes Valium or Ativan are used but may become addictive.

AKATHISIA - Restlessness or muscular discomfort.

AKINESIA - Slow or rigid movement or tremors, mask-like facial expression, shuffling walk.

DYSTONIA - Sudden muscle contractions which often involve neck, back or eyes and may cause breathing difficulty.

RABBIT SYNDROME - Rapid mouth movements.

TD/TARDIVE DYSKINESIA - Involuntary movements of lip, tongue, mouth, face or shoulders, wrists, arms, legs, feet; this is not treated with anticholinergic drugs.

NEUROLEPTIC MALIGNANT SYNDROME - Notify doctor and/or emergency medical services if these develop: high fever, rapid heart beat, rapid breathing, stiff muscles, sweating, shaking, incontinence; stupor; heart and/or kidney and/or blood problems may follow.

Other possible side effects of Antipsychotics include: BLURRED VISION, CONSTIPATION, DECREASED URINATION - Get eye exams and avoid activities requiring good vision until this improves; increase fluid, fiber, exercise, and ask M.D. about stool softeners; urinate before doses; M.D. may prescribe a medicine to treat urinary retention (URECHOLINE / bethanechol).

DRY MOUTH - Use sugarless gum and/or candy, fluids, and ask about artificial saliva. Some newer antipsychotics may increase saliva.

DIZZINESS, RAPID HEARTBEAT, LOW BLOOD PRESSURE - M.D. may order an electrocardiogram; monitor blood pressure lying, sitting and standing, and change positions slowly.

RASH, SUN SENSITIVITY - Notify doctor about rash or itching; use sunscreen and protective clothing.

SORE THROAT, FEVER, FEELING ILL, BLOOD PROBLEMS - Notify M.D.; blood counts will be monitored, (often weekly with Clozaril).

UPSET STOMACH, YELLOW SKIN OR EYES - M.D. will monitor liver function blood tests.

CHANGES IN SEXUAL FUNCTION AND/OR DESIRE; MENSTRUAL AND/OR BREAST CHANGES IN WOMEN; CHANGES IN APPETITE - Talk with M.D. who may change medicine, order blood tests or other exams; proper diet and exercise help maintain stable weight; sometimes body temperature regulation may be affected.

Discuss with M.D. your medical history and/or problems, use of alcohol and/or drugs, prescription or over-the-counter medicines, and any plans for pregnancy or breastfeeding. Some antipsychotics increase likelihood of seizures in some people. Discuss any unusual symptoms and/or side effects with your doctor.

Benzodiazepines include:

VALIUM / diazepam	LIBRIUM / chlordiazepoxide	KLONOPIN / lonazepam
XANAX / alprazolam	ATIVAN / lorazepam	SERAX / oxazepam

ANTIANXIETY MEDICATIONS treat these symptoms: nervousness, panic, fear, 'butterflies in stomach', hyperventilation, nausea, tremulousness and others.

SIDE EFFECTS: Discuss specifics with your M.D. and pharmacist. Medicines in this category may have some of these side effects and considerations plus others. Report persistent and / or troublesome symptoms.

DROWSINESS, DIZZINESS, UNSTEADY WALK - Avoid activities requiring alertness (driving or machine operation); do not smoke alone or in bed. In some people an unexpected opposite effect (irritability or excitement) occurs and M.D. may change the medicine.

FEELINGS OF DETACHMENT OR LESS CONTROL OVER IMPULSES - Be cautious and aware your memory and judgement may be affected; slurred speech, confusion, and severe weakness must be reported immediately.

INCREASED APPETITE AND / OR WEIGHT GAIN - Take with meals, nutritional but low calorie diet, exercise, consult dietician.

NAUSEA, CONFUSION, DEPRESSION - Tell M.D. who may decrease dose or change medication.

HEADACHE - Ask M.D. about over-the-counter pain relievers.

ITCHING AND / OR RASHES - Tell M.D.

HEART PALPITATIONS AND / OR RAPID HEARTBEAT AND LOW BLOOD PRESSURE - Tell M.D., monitor heart rate and blood pressure.

CONSTIPATION AND DRY MOUTH - Increase fluids, fiber, exercise; use sugarless gum and candy.

These medications may become habit-forming and should not be used with alcohol or other sedating drugs as dangerously slow respiration, heartbeat and other functions may occur. Discuss with M.D. your medical history and problems, especially drug or alcohol use or family history of substance abuse. Discuss any plans for pregnancy or breastfeeding. Discuss any prescription and / or over-the-counter medicines as some interact dangerously with benzodiazepines. Report any unusual symptoms and / or side effects to your doctor.

These medications are usually for short-term use but should not be stopped abruptly. M.D. will gradually decrease them. Withdrawal symptoms may include shakiness, agitation, anxiety, restlessness, insomnia, ringing in the ears, diarrhea, muscle twitching, hallucinations, seizures and other serious problems.

BUSPAR / buspirone is used to treat these symptoms: nervousness, panic, fear, 'butterflies in stomach', hyperventilation, nausea, tremulousness and others. It is not a benzodiazepine, is not addictive, and causes fewer side effects and less memory impairment or sedation than other antianxiety medications. See ways to minimize possible side effects noted for the other antianxiety medications (above). Numbness, weakness or tingling in hands and feet may also occur. **Do not use with MAOIs, avoid alcohol, and inform M.D. of any plans for pregnancy or breastfeeding. Discuss with doctor your medical history and problems, especially liver or kidney disorders, and any over-the-counter or prescription medicines you take. Report any unusual symptoms and/or side effects to your doctor.**

Other medications used for anxiety include antihistamines which are not addictive but must be used with caution in some circumstances (such as seizure history), and barbiturates which have addictive potential and pose overdose dangers. **Consult doctor and pharmacist for specifics.** Antianxiety medicines also help you sleep. Other medicines for insomnia include DALMANE/flurazepam and RESTORIL/temazepam. Their side effects and considerations are similar to the benzodiazepines. **Consult doctor and pharmacist for specifics.**

MEDICINE MATCH-UP

WORKSHEET

WORKSHEET FOR MEDICINE INFORMATION SHEETS:
PARTICIPANTS FILL IN THE BLANKS, THEN SHARE INFORMATION WITH GROUP MEMBERS.

1. Name of medication: _____

2. Category (antidepressant, antianxiety, antipsychotic, mood stabilizer): _____

3. List at least five possible side effects and ways to minimize each. _____

_____

_____

_____

_____

_____

4. List at least five things to discuss with doctor. _____

_____

_____

_____

_____

_____

5. What blood/medical tests might be done when on this medication? _____

_____

6. List at least five symptoms that should decrease when on this medication . _____

_____

_____

7. List foods, medicines, substances to avoid when on this medication . _____

_____

_____

_____

PANEL DISCUSSION

AGE	DIFFICULTY	PAGES
A & T	2	2

PURPOSE To verbalize therapeutic concepts and apply them to own life.

MATERIALS Board, marker, 'PANEL DISCUSSION' QUESTIONS AND STATEMENTS, page 100.

ATTENTION GRABBER Arrange chairs around conference table(s).
Ask, "Who has seen a panel discussion on TV?" and discuss process.

ACTIVITY Take turns being 'moderator' (asking the question) and 'panelists'.
Set ground rules – only one person speaks at a time and respects differing views.
Moderator writes question on board before panelists speak.

FOLLOW-UP Each shares a new concept learned today.

PANEL DISCUSSION

QUESTIONS and STATEMENTS

1. Describe benefits of and need for patience with ourselves and others.
2. How do we lose our own identity? How do we find and keep it?
3. What is 'learned helplessness' and how can we learn to help ourselves? Give specific examples of each.
4. What is a self-fulfilling prophecy? Explain how it causes negative and positive results.
5. Explain: Know when to be gentle with yourself and when to kick your own butt.
6. Tell about a time you repressed anger and what was the consequence to you? Tell about a time you repressed fear and what was the consequence to you? Tell about a time you repressed sadness and what was the consequence to you?
7. How does fear of authority figures affect you?
8. How does it help to love your enemies?
9. When have you been an underachiever and how can you achieve your full potential?
10. What emotions are you uncomfortable feeling and expressing?
11. What emotions are you comfortable feeling and expressing?
12. Five ways to increase self-esteem are:
13. What is wrong with being a perfectionist?
14. What is realistic goal setting and why is it important?
15. What happens when we let others control our emotions or behavior and how can we maintain control over our own thoughts, feelings and actions?
16. What are frozen feelings and how do they hurt us? How can we 'thaw' them?
17. Name someone you resent and tell how it affects you. Tell 3 ways to overcome resentment.
18. What happens when we expect others to take care of us? How can we take care of ourselves? (at least ten ways)
19. Your two favorite anger management techniques are:
20. What is the problem with needing approval from others?
21. Tell about your spirituality and how it helps you.
22. What happens when we try to control others? How does it hurt them and us?
23. A time you felt defeated and what you did that was positive:
24. Who or what do you fear and how has it affected you?
25. What does it mean to be consumed by mental illness? How can you place it in perspective?
26. What is a 'people pleaser' and are you one?
27. Who should be in the driver's seat — thoughts or feelings? Why?
28. What do you need to stop procrastinating about and 'just do it'?
29. What happens when we become caretakers (to the other person[s] and us)?
30. Explain: "To Thine Own Self Be True" and how can you be truer to yourself?
31. How can you 'act as if' in a situation when you need confidence, courage, esteem or other attributes?

PICTURE GAME

AGE	DIFFICULTY	PAGES
ALL	1	2

PURPOSE

Identify coping skills and apply to current situations.

MATERIALS

Board, marker, container for CUT-UPS,
'PICTURE GAME' CUT-UPS, page 102.

ATTENTION GRABBER

Volunteer explains how to play the Picture Game.
No speaking or writing.
If someone cannot draw the concept, acting it out, as in Charades, is allowed.

ACTIVITY

First person selects slip, draws the coping skill (example – "call a friend or therapist" – s/he depicts stick figures and a telephone). First guesser tells how this skill will help him/her face a current situation. If guesser had a turn, s/he selects someone who hasn't.

FOLLOW-UP

Each tells a new technique s/he learned today.

PICTURE GAME

1 Ride a bike.	**2** Take a walk.	**3** Swim.
4 Take a shower.	**5** Take a bath.	**6** Take a nap.
7 Call someone.	**8** Take medicines as prescribed.	**9** Draw.
10 Journal.	**11** Play sports.	**12** Watch sports.
13 Go to the park.	**14** Read a book.	**15** Watch a comedy on TV.
16 Go to the movies.	**17** Sing.	**18** Dance.
19 Take a deep breath.	**20** Wear new clothes.	**21** Think positive.
22 Get a new haircut and/or style.	**23** Wear make-up.	**24** Wear nail polish.

FACILITATOR'S INFORMATION
TIC-TAC-COPE

AGE	DIFFICULTY	PAGES
ALL	2	3

PURPOSE
Identify alternatives, develop insight and promote positive peer pressure for healthy handling of feelings versus self-harm.

MATERIALS
Board, marker, 'TIC-TAC-COPE' QUESTIONS, page 104, and ANSWER SHEET, page 105. (Optional) journals, paper, crayons suggested as prizes to encourage appropriate expression of feelings, or play money ('SKILLS BILLS', pages 277, 278).

ATTENTION GRABBER
Volunteer writes on board and elicits related words and phrases from peers:
S - E - L - F   H - A - R - M
Examples: **S** = Suicide is not an option
E = Express feelings safely
L = Love yourself unconditionally
F = Find supportive people
H = Help each other stay safe
A = Accept what cannot be changed
R = Reach out to others who are hurting
M = Make a contract for safety with yourself and others

ACTIVITY
'Game Show Host' draws Tic-Tac-Toe game on board. Two teams sit facing each other with 'Host' at board in front. At bottom of board note players' names under 'X' or 'O' and keep score (number of games won by each team). 'Host' asks alternate teams the questions; a correct answer warrants an 'X' or 'O'; teammates should collaborate on answers and some questions require two or more people to respond. If they answer incorrectly, the opposition tries. Continue until one team wins or all spaces are filled. If a tie occurs, the next question is the tie- breaker. Whichever team answers correctly first, wins. Erase board, appoint another 'Host' and continue until all questions have been answered. Winners get first choice of prizes; the opponents select from the remaining prizes. If no tangible rewards are available, discuss what everyone 'won' in terms of coping skills.

FOLLOW-UP
Discuss value of a support group for safety wherein people pledge to tell group members, (and staff), immediately when impulses occur or at the first 'warning signs' of anger and/or depression in self or others. Encourage daily 'success stories' about times they felt like cutting, purging or other destructive acts, but used coping skills instead. Consider graphs showing number of 'safe' days (each draws and/or records own progress).

VARIATION
I. Distribute question sheets about 20 minutes before game. Teams go to separate areas to discuss and/or write answers, then use their 'cheat sheets' during the game.

II. Individuals, dyads or teams:
1. make "NO SELF HARM" posters using drawings, stick figures, cartoons and symbols; display on walls.
2. compose poetry and/or songs promoting self- care and share with group.
3. create 'Infomercials', monologues or skits to convince 'viewers' to act safely in stressful situations. (Example: role-play partners breaking up; the jilted lover thinks about cutting his/her wrist, then calls a support person instead).
4. select a term and compose helpful messages.
Examples: **A** = A strong feeling   **C** = Cop-out
N = Never stuff anger   **U** = Understand feelings
G = Get your feelings out safely   **T** = Think about options
E = Everyone feels mad at times
R = Recognize early warning signs of anger, depression and cravings

103

TIC-TAC-COPE

1. Give 3 examples of self-harm.

2. Name 3 emotions that cause some people to think about self-harm.

3. Name 3 consequences of self-harm.

4. What is the major drawback of self-harm?

5. What is a 'quick-fix'?

6. What are at least 3 examples of 'quick-fixes'?

7. What is not helpful about 'quick-fixes'?

8. What is more helpful than 'quick-fixes'?

9. What is peer pressure?

10. Tell a time you felt pressure to do something harmful.

11. Tell a time someone influenced you to do something helpful to yourself.

12. What is a support group?

13. Why can people with similar problems help each other effectively?

14. How could you help a person who wants to hurt himself / herself?

15. What are at least 2 healthy ways to let out your feelings of sadness or anger?

16. What are early warning signs of anger?

17. What are 2 early warning signs of depression?

18. How might medications help people who hurt themselves?

19. How might individual therapy help?

20. How might family therapy help?

21. Who is responsible or who causes someone to harm himself / herself?

22. Yes or No — can we control what others say or do?

23. What or who can we control?

TIC-TAC-COPE

ANSWER SHEET

1. **Give 3 examples of self-harm.**
   Cutting, suicide attempts, purging, starving, drugs, alcohol and others

2. **Name 3 emotions that cause some people to think about self-harm.**
   Anger, depression, craving excitement, guilt, low esteem and others

3. **Name 3 consequences of self-harm.** *Scars, being hospitalized, health problems, death*

4. **What is the major drawback of self-harm?** *We do not solve the problem that led to it – we still have the anger, depression or conflict with someone*

5. **What is a 'quick-fix'?** *Something that seems to give relief at the moment*

6. **What are at least 3 examples of 'quick-fixes'?** *Cutting, punching walls, banging heads, drinking, drugs and others*

7. **What is not helpful about 'quick-fixes'?** *They do not last*

8. **What is more helpful than 'quick-fixes'?**
   Facing and solving problems, prescribed medication, therapy, coping skills and others

9. **What is peer pressure?** *People similar to ourselves or our friends influencing us*

10. **Tell a time you felt pressure to do something harmful.**
    At least 2 people on the team must share

11. **Tell a time someone influenced you to do something helpful to yourself.**
    At least 2 people on the team must share

12. **What is a support group?** *People with same problems help each other*

13. **Why can people with similar problems help each other effectively?**
    First-hand experience, accessibility

14. **How could you help a person who wants to hurt himself/herself?** *Listen, suggest ways to deal with the problem and tell the family, therapist or the police if they are in danger*

15. **What are at least 2 healthy ways to let out your feelings of sadness or anger?**
    Talk, draw, write and others

16. **What are early warning signs of anger?** (At least 2 people share)
    Clenched fists, rapid breathing and heartbeat, red face

17. **What are 2 early warning signs of depression?**
    Sleep more or less, eat more or less, very tired or restless, teary eyed, isolated

18. **How might medications help people who hurt themselves?** *Stabilize a chemical imbalance*

19. **How might individual therapy help?**
    Find out what's really bugging them and ways to handle problems

20. **How might family therapy help?** *Solve problems, open communication*

21. **Who is responsible or who causes someone to harm him/herself?** *Himself/herself*

22. **Yes or No – can we control what others say or do?** *No*

23. **What or who can we control?** *Our own reactions*

Tic-Tac-Medicine

AGE	DIFFICULTY	PAGES
ALL	2	3

PURPOSE

Identify purposes, minimize adverse effects and related medication information.

MATERIALS

Board, marker, 'TIC-TAC-MEDICINE' QUESTIONS, page 107, and ANSWER SHEET, page 108. (Optional) prizes or play money (SKILLS BILLS, pages 277, 278).

ATTENTION GRABBER

Volunteer draws tic-tac-toe lines on board.
Two teams face each other and claim 'X' or 'O'.

ACTIVITY

'Game Show Host' draws Tic-Tac-Toe game on board. Two teams sit facing each other with 'Host' at board in front. At bottom of board note players' names under 'X' or 'O' and keep score (number of games won by each team). 'Host' asks alternate teams the questions; a correct answer warrants an 'X' or 'O'; teammates should collaborate on answers and some questions require two or more people to respond. If they answer incorrectly, the opposition tries. Continue until one team wins or all spaces are filled. If a tie occurs, the next question is the tie-breaker. Whichever team answers correctly first, wins. Erase board, appoint another 'Host' and continue until all questions have been answered. Winners get first choice of prizes; the opponents select from the remaining prizes. If no tangible rewards are available, discuss what everyone 'won' in terms of coping skills.

FOLLOW-UP

Each tells one medicine fact learned during group.

Tic-Tac-Medicine

QUESTIONS

1. Does taking medicine mean you are crazy?

2. What is an antidepressant?

3. Name an antidepressant.

4. What does 'side effect' mean?

5. Give an example of a side effect.

6. If a medicine upsets your stomach, what might help?

7. If you get dizzy when you jump up quickly, what should you do?

8. A person has been on medicine for 3 days and doesn't feel any better. What should s/he do?

9. What happens if you drink alcohol while taking medicine?

10. What is a hallucination?

11. What does it mean if a medicine is addictive?

12. What symptoms do antipsychotic medicines treat?

13. Name a medicine that helps people who hear voices.

14. What are mood swings?

15. What medicines help with mood swings?

16. What are coping skills?

17. Which is better – medicine or coping skills?

18. You have been on a medicine for 2 months and feel no better or worse – what should you do?

19. If a person is on medicines, how long should s/he take them?

20. When is a shot better than a pill?

21. Why are blood tests done when on some medicines?

22. Why should antianxiety medicines be taken for only a short time?

Tic-Tac-Medicine

ANSWER SHEET

1. **Does taking medicine mean you are crazy?** *No, you may have a chemical imbalance*

2. **What is an antidepressant?** *Treats severe and continuous sadness*

3. **Name an antidepressant.** *Prozac, Paxil, Zoloft, Effexor, Wellbutrin or others*

4. **What does 'side effect' mean?** *Unwanted effect*

5. **Give an example of a side effect.**
   Dry mouth, sedation, lightheaded, stomach upset, blurry vision and others

6. **If a medicine upsets your stomach, what might help?** *Take it with food*

7. **If you get dizzy when you jump up quickly, what should you do?** *Change position slowly*

8. **A person has been on medicine for 3 days and doesn't feel any better. What should s/he do?**
   Contact M.D., give it 4-6 weeks

9. **What happens if you drink alcohol while taking medicine?**
   Could die or effects will be intensified or minimized

10. **What is a hallucination?** *Seeing, hearing, feeling, smelling, tasting something that is not real*

11. **What does it mean if a medicine is addictive?** *Your body has to have more and more of it*

12. **What symptoms do antipsychotic medicines treat?**
    Delusions, paranoia, hallucinations, thought disorders

13. **Name a medicine that helps people who hear voices.** *Zyprexa, Risperdal, Haldol, or others*

14. **What are mood swings?** *Happy, sad, mad, up and down*

15. **What medicines help with mood swings?**
    Mood stabilizers – Depakote, Lithium, Tegretol, Neurontin

16. **What are coping skills?** *Ways to think and act when upset, angry or sad*

17. **Which is better – medicine or coping skills?**
    Trick question – answer is "neither" or "both". "Neither is better" or " both are equally helpful"

18. **You have been on a medicine for 2 months and feel no better or worse – what should you do?**
    Tell your doctor

19. **If a person is on medicines, how long should s/he take them?**
    Probably at least 6-9 months or for as long as doctor believes they are necessary

20. **When is a shot better than a pill?** *Quick action*

21. **Why are blood tests done when on some medicines?** *To check blood levels of the medicine and/or to be sure kidney, liver or other organs are functioning normally*

22. **Why should antianxiety medicines be taken for only a short time?** *They can be addictive and people need to learn stress reduction techniques*

TWENTY-ONE

AGE	DIFFICULTY	PAGES
A & T	3	6

PURPOSE

To identify and apply mental health concepts.

MATERIALS

Board, marker, 'TWENTY-ONE' QUESTIONS, pages 110-113, and ANSWER SHEET, page 114.
If available, computer screen, transparencies and overhead projector to show one question at a time.

ATTENTION GRABBER

Volunteer writes '21' on board. Ask group if they've ever played the card game or watched the TV show. Explain "The first team to get 21 points wins."

ACTIVITY

Divide into 2 teams. 'Game Show Host' alternately questions both teams.
Members take turns answering. There is one best answer to each question.
They may collaborate but only one final answer is considered.
If wrong, the opponents answer.
The opposing team also answers the next question.
Scorekeeper notes points on board.
The lower number questions are easier; 11 point questions are most difficult.
People select their own level of difficulty.

FOLLOW-UP

Each shares the most important concepts s/he learned today.

VARIATION

Dyads or teams receive the written questions and collaborate on the answers. Then the whole group discusses responses and scores their sheets. Dyad or team with the highest number of correct responses wins.

TWENTY-ONE

1. Which is the earliest sign of anger?
   a) red face and clenched fists
   b) punching walls
   c) negative thoughts
   d) staring or giving dirty looks

2. In the heat of anger, which should you do first?
   a) talk it out
   b) tell the other person to calm down
   c) walk away
   d) reach a compromise

3. Which is most likely to lead to depression?
   a) change in schools
   b) death of partner
   c) trouble with boss
   d) bankruptcy

4. What is Manic-Depression or Bipolar Disorder?
   a) extreme mood swings
   b) severe depression
   c) paranoia
   d) hallucinations

5. Fear of abandonment, being made to look foolish and lack of control over a situation are frequent causes of:
   a) delusions
   b) hallucinations
   c) anger
   d) mood swings

6. Extreme nervousness, fast heartbeat, fast breathing, and fear are symptoms of:
   a) psychosis
   b) insanity
   c) anxiety
   d) depression

7. Eating much more or less, excessive sleep or insomnia and lack of pleasure or interest in activities are symptoms of:
   a) anxiety
   b) depression
   c) mania
   d) irritability

8. Low levels of which chemicals in the brain are linked with depression?
   a) insulin and bile
   b) glucose and lactose
   c) serotonin and dopamine
   d) estrogen and testosterone

9. Loss of interest, poor memory and judgement are symptoms of:
   a) dementia
   b) obsessive-compulsive disorder
   c) manic-depression
   d) anxiety disorder

10. Cognitive therapy involves:
    a) dream analysis
    b) delving into your childhood
    c) group therapy
    d) changing negative or distorted thoughts

11. Repetitive thoughts and behaviors like constant hand washing or checking things, like locks or stoves, are symptoms of:
    a) manic-depression
    b) paranoid delusions
    c) adjustment disorder of adolescence
    d) obsessive-compulsive disorder

Twenty-One

1. To treat a chemical imbalance we use:
   a) therapy
   b) medicine
   c) alcohol
   d) support groups

2. Intense fear for no real reason is a symptom of:
   a) depression
   b) dysthymia
   c) panic
   d) hypersomnia

3. Endorphins are:
   a) brain chemicals
   b) digestive juices
   c) dwarfs
   d) dolphins

4. A natural salt used to treat Bipolar Disorder is:
   a) rock salt
   b) table salt
   c) Lithium
   d) Depakote

5. Problems of husbands, wives, children are addressed in:
   a) support groups
   b) psychoanalysis
   c) aversive therapy
   d) family therapy

6. Fear of a specific thing like heights or water is a :
   a) phobia
   b) delusion
   c) hallucination
   d) craving

7. In psychosis, people experience:
   a) extreme sadness
   b) mood swings
   c) delusions and hallucinations
   d) anxiety and fear

8. Stuffing our thoughts or feelings to the point we are unaware of them is:
   a) rejection
   b) regression
   c) repression
   d) regeneration

9. Going back to an earlier time or a more childish behavior is:
   a) denial
   b) blaming
   c) projection
   d) regression

10. Unhealthy defenses used in addiction are mainly:
    a) denial and blaming
    b) conversion and compromise
    c) sublimation and suggestion
    d) moderation and accountability

11. The most important component of recovery from substance abuse is:
    a) medication for underlying depression
    b) weekly therapy sessions
    c) family support
    d) working the 12 steps and attending meetings

Twenty-One

1. **Deep breathing and exercise help control:**
   a) voices and visions
   b) delusions and paranoia
   c) anxiety and anger
   d) adjustment disorders

2. **Time-out means:**
   a) leave the situation forever
   b) never talk about the problems
   c) leave temporarily until you calm down
   d) take a break for booze or drugs

3. **Jealousy is caused by:**
   a) someone who is better looking or smarter
   b) someone with more money
   c) comparing ourself with someone else
   d) people who brag

4. **I feel angry when I'm jealous because:**
   a) the person thinks I'm not as good
   b) I think I'm not as good
   c) Others think I'm not as good
   d) I'm really not as good

5. **To avoid jealousy, realize:**
   a) everyone has special talents
   b) I can always try to top him / her
   c) I can do something to make the person look bad
   d) I can avoid being around the person

6. **If my partner leaves me:**
   a) it's the end of the world
   b) he or she might come back
   c) eventually I'll love again
   d) I'll never trust anyone

7. **If I fail a test:**
   a) I'm stupid
   b) I'm smart and the instructor is stupid
   c) I need tutoring and better study habits
   d) I should quit the class or leave school

8. **If someone wants to have sex, I should:**
   a) slap his/her face
   b) jump in bed
   c) consider possible consequences
   d) tell him/her maybe next time

9. **I have been clean and sober for 6 weeks. Now I can:**
   a) fall in love
   b) drink in moderation
   c) continue step-work and meetings
   d) take on a new job or start a full schedule of college classes

10. **If I'm being abused, I should:**
    a) suffer in silence
    b) threaten to kill the abuser
    c) tell the abuser I'm going to tell on him/her
    d) tell a teacher, counselor, therapist, doctor, nurse or police officer

11. **I want to remain sober, so I:**
    a) go to a booze party but sip soda or juice
    b) stay home and feel lonely
    c) go and drink one beer only
    d) go to a meeting or an activity where no alcohol is served

TWENTY-ONE

1. Picturing a calm scene or ourselves performing successfully is:
   a) visualization
   b) visual hallucination
   c) vivid imagination
   d) wishful thinking

2. If we expect the worst of ourselves, we usually:
   a) do well
   b) do poorly
   c) expectations have no effect on our performance
   d) won't give up

3. If we treat people with respect, they usually:
   a) treat us like poop
   b) take advantage of us
   c) treat us with respect
   d) ignore us

4. If we dislike rules or policies, we should:
   a) suffer in silence
   b) violate them outright
   c) discuss them with rule-makers
   d) find a sneaky way to violate them

5. If I make a mistake, I should:
   a) cover it up
   b) admit it
   c) blame someone
   d) feel like a failure

6. If someone is rude or talks about me behind my back, I should:
   a) do the same to him / her
   b) suffer in silence
   c) talk calmly to the person, starting with "I feel ..."
   d) talk calmly to the person, asking, "Why do you ...?"

7. If a friend tells me a secret about suicide or homicide, I should:
   a) keep the secret
   b) talk him/her out of it
   c) make him/her a psychiatry appointment
   d) immediately tell the police or the person's family and/or counselor

8. People who talk about suicide or homicide:
   a) never do it
   b) just want attention
   c) often do it
   d) should be ignored

9. Which statement is true?
   a) we cannot help how we feel
   b) if we change our thoughts, our feelings and actions will change
   c) we will forever be victims of our past
   d) some people are born losers

10. The best ways to handle emotional problems are:
    a) denial and ignoring them
    b) prescribed medication and therapy
    c) self-harm (cutting our wrists or overdosing)
    d) drinking and/or drugs for long-lasting relief

11. An example of an environmental stressor is :
    a) poverty
    b) genes
    c) body chemistry
    d) low IQ

TWENTY-ONE

ANSWER SHEET

A.	B.	C.	D.
1. c	1. b	1. c	1. a
2. c	2. c	2. c	2. b
3. b	3. a	3. c	3. c
4. a	4. c	4. b	4. c
5. c	5. d	5. a	5. b
6. c	6. a	6. c	6. c
7. b	7. c	7. c	7. d
8. c	8. c	8. c	8. c
9. a	9. d	9. c	9. b
10. d	10. a	10. d	10. b
11. d	11. d	11. d	11. a

FACILITATOR'S INFORMATION
WHO WANTS TO BE
A PILLIONAIRE?

AGE	DIFFICULTY	PAGES
A & T	3	6

PURPOSE

Identify medication and mental health concepts.

MATERIALS

Board, marker, 'WHO WANTS TO BE A PILLIONAIRE' QUESTIONS, pages 116-119, and ANSWER SHEET, page 120. If available, use computer screen, transparencies and overhead projector to show one question at a time.
Play money ('SKILLS BILLS', pages 277, 278).

ATTENTION GRABBER

Ask who has seen "Who Wants To Be A Millionaire?," and explain we'll play a similar game.
Volunteer writes, "Who Wants To Be A Pillionaire?" on board.
Explain they must pick the one <u>best</u> answer to each question.

ACTIVITY

Divide into two teams (A and B).
Place chairs in rows, facing each other with 'Game Show Host' and 'Spotlight Seat' in front.
Designated 'Host' has list of questions worth $100,000 each.
First person from Team A takes 'Spotlight Seat' and answers first question, using team members as 'lifelines'. One or several may help but only one 'final answer' is allowed.
    Correct answer warrants $100,000.
Keep score on board. If incorrect, Team B gets opportunity.
Team B's first person goes to 'spotlight seat', answers the others team's missed question, gets $100,000 and may then answer another question (their own).
    If Team A answered correctly, Team B still goes next and answers their own first question.
    Teams alternately send members to 'spotlight seat' to gain 'money.'
Team who reaches $1,000,000 first wins.

FOLLOW-UP

Each tells most valuable fact learned today.

VARIATION

Distribute question sheets to both teams.
Teammates go to separate corners or rooms and collaborate on answers in advance.

115

WHO WANTS TO BE A PILLIONAIRE?

QUESTIONS page 1

1. What is best used to treat a chemical imbalance in the brain?
   a) food
   b) water
   c) medicine
   d) therapy

2. An antidepressant treats:
   a) hallucinations
   b) fear
   c) anxiety
   d) sadness

3. An antipsychotic treats:
   a) bad moods
   b) thought disorder
   c) heart problems
   d) nervousness

4. A paranoid person:
   a) distrusts people
   b) loves people
   c) hates animals
   d) acts silly

5. A person who sees, hears, smells, tastes or feels things that are not there is experiencing:
   a) mood swings
   b) hallucinations
   c) anxiety
   d) delusions

6. A false belief is a:
   a) dream
   b) lie
   c) memory
   d) delusion

7. Paxil is an:
   a) antibiotic
   b) antidepressant
   c) antipsychotic
   d) illegal drug

8. Risperdal and Zyprexa help people with:
   a) delusions and hallucinations
   b) hives and rashes
   c) stomach upsets
   d) anger and depression

9. If medicine upsets your stomach:
   a) take Mylanta with every dose
   b) take it with food or milk
   c) give it to an enemy
   d) take it and suffer

10. If you get dizzy when you go from lying down to standing up quickly, you should:
    a) quit your pills
    b) jump up to answer the phone
    c) take rapid shallow breaths
    d) change positions slowly

11. The best thing for dry mouth is:
    a) soda pop
    b) bubble gum
    c) chocolate candy bar
    d) sugarless gum or hard candy

12. If you are constipated:
    a) increase fluid, bulk and exercise
    b) take laxative every day
    c) forget about it
    d) push real hard

13. A person with Bipolar Disorder suffers from:
    a) North Pole Fever
    b) extreme highs and lows
    c) molar cavities
    d) bigamy

14. Anger turned inward sometimes becomes:
    a) depression
    b) anxiety
    c) psychosis
    d) halitosis

116

WHO WANTS TO BE A PILLIONAIRE?

15. An addictive medicine is:
    a) expensive
    b) habit-forming
    c) rare
    d) unpleasant

16. Depakote, Lithium, Tegretol, and Neurontin are used to treat:
    a) anxiety
    b) depression
    c) psychosis
    d) mood swings

17. Which is better?
    a) medicine
    b) coping skills
    c) neither is useful
    d) both can be equally helpful

18. Drinking alcohol while on medication is:
    a) fun
    b) against the law
    c) dangerous
    d) helpful

19. Exercise can:
    a) improve mood and decrease anger and anxiety
    b) increase depression
    c) make hallucinations stronger
    d) make highs higher and lows lower

20. Psychotropic medicine might:
    a) control your mind
    b) help you control impulses
    c) make you crazy
    d) make people dislike you

21. If medicine makes you drowsy:
    a) drive your car slowly
    b) ride a bike
    c) do not drive or operate machinery
    d) ask doctor if you can take it every morning

22. A therapeutic blood level of medicine means:
    a) too little
    b) too much
    c) the right amount
    d) you are not anemic

23. Which organs help get rid of the medication wastes?
    a) heart and lungs
    b) thyroid and pancreas
    c) ovaries and testicles
    d) liver and kidneys

24. A side effect of some antipsychotic medications is:
    a) muscle stiffness
    b) hearing voices
    c) seeing visions
    d) stuffy nose

25. A rash after taking medication usually means:
    a) you got into poison ivy
    b) you have measles
    c) an allergic reaction
    d) prickly heat

26. Psychotropic medicines affect:
    a) brain chemicals
    b) stomach enzymes
    c) blood gasses
    d) bones

27. If your depression, mood swings, paranoia or voices are better, you should:
    a) quit your medicine
    b) continue medicine forever
    c) take higher doses
    d) tell your doctor

28. If your sex life is affected by medicine:
    a) keep it a secret
    b) tell your doctor
    c) throw away your pills
    d) give the medicine to your partner

117

WHO WANTS TO BE A PILLIONAIRE?

29. If you sunburn more easily when taking medicine, you should tell your doctor and:
    a) wear sunscreen and protective clothes
    b) stay inside
    c) don't take your medicine before going to the beach
    d) go outside at night only

30. A toxic blood level of medicine means:
    a) too little
    b) too much
    c) the right amount
    d) none in your blood

31. Medications for Attention Deficit Disorders are:
    a) Aspirin and Tylenol
    b) Haldol and Cogentin
    c) Ritalin and Cylert
    d) Dilantin and Tegretol

32. If your medications keeps you awake:
    a) take extra before bed
    b) ask doctor if you can take it only in the morning
    c) take it when you want to study or watch late night TV
    d) give it to a lazy person

33. If you have unpleasant side effects:
    a) tell your doctor
    b) quit your medicine immediately
    c) sell your medication
    d) take it and suffer

34. Brain chemicals that make us feel better are:
    a) insulin and lactose
    b) bile and bilirubin
    c) serotonin and dopamine
    d) oxygen and carbon dioxide

35. Anticonvulsants prevent:
    a) anxiety
    b) seizures
    c) depression
    d) strokes

36. Which tests the electrical activity in the brain?
    a) treadmill
    b) EKG
    c) stethoscope
    d) EEG

37. Which tests electrical activity of the heart?
    a) angiogram
    b) sonogram
    c) EKG
    d) ultrasound

38. If you become pregnant while on medication:
    a) continue the medicine
    b) stop the medicine
    c) tell doctor immediately
    d) take prenatal vitamins

39. Which doctor can prescribe medications?
    a) psychologist
    b) psychiatrist
    c) neither
    d) both

40. If a medicine does not seem to help after one week:
    a) double the dose
    b) continue as prescribed
    c) throw it away
    d) tell your doctor immediately

41. If a medicine does not help after 6 weeks:
    a) tell your doctor immediately
    b) get a refund from the drug store
    c) flush it down the toilet
    d) double the dose

42. **If you are an alcoholic:**
    a) take no psychiatric medicines
    b) inform your doctor of alcoholism so appropriate medication and tapering (if needed) are prescribed
    c) take Valium for your nerves
    d) take codeine for pain

43. **Mental illness can be caused by:**
    a) chemical imbalance
    b) environmental stressors
    c) heredity
    d) any or all of these

44. **Support groups like AA (Alcoholics Anonymous) or EA (Emotions Anonymous) or OA (Overeaters Anonymous) help because:**
    a) people with similar problems help each other
    b) nurses and doctors help patients
    c) social workers and counselors help people
    d) they often have parties

45. **Can mental illness be inherited?**
    a) always
    b) never
    c) sometimes
    d) only from mother to daughter or father to son

46. **Can we recover emotionally from severe physical or sexual abuse?**
    a) never
    b) always
    c) with appropriate treatment
    d) only if we take revenge on the perpetrator

47. **To prevent running out of medicine:**
    a) take it every other day instead of daily
    b) cut your pills in half
    c) call the pharmacy or doctor when you have one week's supply left
    d) go to the emergency room when you use your last pill

48. **Which is crazy behavior:**
    a) refusing medicine that will help
    b) taking medicine as prescribed
    c) going to therapy appointments
    d) asking your doctor about side effects

49. **If you are on Lithium:**
    a) avoid chocolate
    b) take adequate milk and cheese
    c) get adequate salt and water
    d) take your medicine 2 hours before your blood is drawn

50. **With medication and counseling, symptoms can be:**
    a) cured
    b) controlled
    c) worsened
    d) forgotten

WHO WANTS TO BE A PILLIONAIRE?

ANSWER SHEET

1 . c	26 . a
2 . d	27 . d
3 . b	28 . b
4 . a	29 . a
5 . b	30 . b
6 . d	31 . c
7 . b	32 . b
8 . a	33 . a
9 . b	34 . c
10 . d	35 . b
11 . d	36 . d
12 . a	37 . c
13 . b	38 . c
14 . a	39 . b
15 . b	40 . b
16 . d	41 . a
17 . d	42 . b
18 . c	43 . d
19 . a	44 . a
20 . b	45 . c
21 . c	46 . c
22 . c	47 . c
23 . d	48 . a
24 . a	49 . c
25 . c	50 . b

INSPIRATION

INSPIRATION is essential, particularly during troubled times. Doctrines are not dictated. People tap into the wisdom of the ages, their Higher Power and inner strength. Poetry and quotations provide hope and help.

ACTIVITY	PAGE NUMBERS	AGE	LEVEL OF DIFFICULTY	PAGES
If You Can	123 - 124	A & T	2	2
Mud or Stars	125 - 127	ALL	2	3
Things to be Desired	128 - 129	A & T	2	2
Words of Wisdom	130 - 131	A & T	2	2

If You Can...

AGE	DIFFICULTY	PAGES
A, T	2	2

PURPOSE ▶ To identify positive traits and triumphs.

MATERIALS ▶ Board, marker, pencils, 'IF YOU CAN ...' WORKSHEET, page 124.

ATTENTION GRABBER ▶ Volunteer writes on board: "If you can _____, you'll be a man" and records as peers brainstorm words to fill in the blank.

Volunteer writes on board: "If you can _____, you'll be a woman" and records as peers brainstorm words to fill in the blank. (Allow superficial, literal and humorous responses at this point.)

ACTIVITY ▶ Explain "We are going to read a poem and 'Man' applies to both sexes". Distribute worksheet with "If" by Rudyard Kipling and related questions. Read in unison a few times. Then people take turns selecting and writing two lines on board and applying the advice to themselves.

FOLLOW-UP ▶ Individuals complete worksheet questions. Whole group then discusses answers.

VARIATION ▶ I. Facilitator or volunteers ask worksheet questions while participants answer orally.

II. Divide into dyads. Each questions partner, records responses, then 'presents' partner to the group and encourages feedback. "This is Amber. A time she trusted herself was..."

If You Can . . .

WORKSHEET

If

If you can keep your head when all about you
　Are losing theirs and blaming it on you,
If you can trust yourself when all men doubt you,
　But make allowance for their doubting too;
If you can wait and not be tired by waiting,
　Or being lied about, don't deal in lies,
Or being hated, don't give way to hating,
　And yet don't look too good, nor talk too wise:

If you can dream – and not make dreams your master;
　If you can think – and not make thoughts your aim;
If you can meet with Triumph and Disaster
　And treat those two imposters the same;
If you can bear to hear the truth you've spoken
　Twisted by knaves to make a trap for fools,
Or watch the things you gave your life to, broken,
　And stoop and build 'em up with worn-out tools:

If you can make one heap of all your winnings
　And risk it on one turn of pitch-and-toss,
And lose, and start again at your beginnings
　And never breathe a word about your loss;
If you can force your heart and nerve and sinew
　To serve your turn long after they are gone,
And so hold on when there is nothing in you
　Except the Will which says to them: "Hold on!"

If you can talk with crowds and keep your virtue,
　Or walk with Kings – nor lose the common touch,
If neither foes nor loving friends can hurt you,
　If all men count with you, but none too much;
If you can fill the unforgiving minute
　With sixty seconds' worth of distance run,
Yours is the Earth and everything that's in it,
　And – which is more – you'll be a Man, my son!
　　　　　　　　　　by Rudyard Kipling

* "If" is reprinted by permission of A.P. Watt Ltd., on behalf of The National Trust for Places of Historical Interest of Natural Beauty, London.

Tell the most recent or significant time you:

1. Kept your head _____
_____

2. Trusted yourself _____
_____

3. Waited _____
_____

4. Didn't deal in lies _____
_____

5. Didn't give way to hating _____
_____

6. Met triumph _____
_____

7. Met disaster _____
_____

8. Built –up broken dreams _____
_____

9. Took a healthy risk _____
_____

10. Started again _____
_____

11. Held on _____
_____

12. Kept your virtue _____
_____

13. Did not let friends or foes hurt you _____
_____

14. Regarding Triumph and Disaster, why should we 'treat these two impostors the same'?
_____

15. How do 'all men count with you, but none too much'? _____
_____

16. How can you 'fill the unforgiving minute with sixty seconds worth of distance run'?
_____
_____

For numbers 17 through 20, read the poem carefully and discuss the four concepts most relevant to your life today

17. _____
_____

18. _____
_____

19. _____
_____

20. _____
_____

MUD OR STARS?

AGE	DIFFICULTY	PAGES
ALL	2	3

PURPOSE

To see the positive aspects of difficult situations; derive benefits from adversity.

MATERIALS

Board, marker, pencils, crayons, paper, (optional) small container of soil or mud, two stars from yellow or white construction paper, 'MUD OR STARS?' WORKSHEET, page 126, SUGGESTED ANSWERS, page 127. (Optional) play money ('SKILLS BILLS', pages 277, 278).

ATTENTION GRABBER

Volunteers take turns drawing on board until picture is complete: one stick figure with eyes looking down and a frown; one stick figure with eyes looking up and a smile; a puddle below labeled "mud"; stars above; jail-like bars in front of the stick figures.

Optional Role-Play: Instead of the board drawing, two volunteers are coached before group one stands in front of room with container of soil or mud at his/her feet, frowning. The other stands next to him/her, a star in each hand held high above head, looking up at stars, smiling.

Write on board: "Two men look out through the same bars; one sees the mud, and one the stars", by Frederick Langbridge. * (From *Shoot For The Moon* by Meiji Stewart, copyright 1996 by Meiji Stewart. Reprinted by permission of Hazelden Foundation, Center City, MN.)

ACTIVITY

Ask, What's going on in the picture (or role-play)?" Elicit that the person looking at mud is sad; person focusing on stars is happier; both are in the same situation.

Ask, "How does this relate to us?" Elicit that participants are or have been in difficult situations analogous to being behind bars. Whether they focus on negatives ('mud'), or positives ('stars'), determines their mood.

Volunteer lists as peers give examples of 'bars'. (Possible answers include abusive relationships; mental illness; substance abuse; problems with family, partner, finances; medical problems; losses.)

Elicit verbal examples of negative 'mud' and 'positive' stars (thoughts, feelings and actions), for each situation listed on board.

Divide into two teams. 'Game Show Host' reads 'MUD OR STARS?' WORKSHEET items to alternating teams. "Team A" answers item #1, "Team B" answers item #2, "Team A" answers item #3, and so forth. Teammates collaborate on answers. To earn one point or play money, they must state a negative and positive thought, feeling and action for each situation listed under 'BARS'. If one team cannot answer, opponents try. Team with the most points or play money wins.

FOLLOW-UP

Distribute paper, pencils and crayons. Instruct people to divide paper into thirds, horizontally. On the middle section, they show themselves in their current most difficult situation, behind 'bars'. This should be personalized and specific, not merely a repeat of an example discussed above. On bottom third they show their 'mud'; on top third they show their 'stars'. Encourage them to draw, symbolize, use stick figures or cartoons and/or write descriptive words phrases to convey the negative and positive aspects of their situations. Then take turns in the 'spotlight seat' showing and telling about their pictures and receiving peer feedback.

Discuss how they have benefited from past adversity by developing strength of character, compassion, faith and coping skills.

VARIATION

I. Teams go to separate rooms or corners about fifteen minutes prior to game. Distribute worksheets and pencils. Teammates confer and note their responses in advance.

II. Individuals or dyads record responses, then share with whole group.

MUD OR STARS?

WORKSHEET

BARS	MUD	STARS
1. Abusive relationships	1.	1.
	2.	2.
	3.	3.
2. Mental illness	1.	1.
	2.	2.
	3.	3.
3. Substance abuse	1.	1.
	2.	2.
	3.	3.
4. Family or partner problems	1.	1.
	2.	2.
	3.	3.
5. Financial problems	1.	1.
	2.	2.
	3.	3.
6. Medical problems	1.	1.
	2.	2.
	3.	3.
7. Losses	1.	1.
	2.	2.
	3.	3.

MUD OR STARS?

Elicit verbal examples of 'mud' or negative thoughts, feelings and actions for each situation, such as:

ABUSIVE RELATIONSHIPS: "I deserve to be mistreated"; feeling worthless; attempting self-harm or staying trapped.

MENTAL ILLNESS: "I'm ruined for life"; feeling hopeless; refusing medication and therapy.

SUBSTANCE ABUSE: "There's nothing to look forward to if I can't drink or use drugs"; craving the 'highs'; relapsing.

FAMILY OR PARTNER PROBLEMS: "We'll never get along"; feeling angry; avoiding communication or compromise; refusing family or relationship counseling.

FINANCIAL PROBLEMS: "I'll never be able to pay my bills or afford necessities"; feeling helpless; ignoring or running from responsibilities; settling for lack of housing, food, transportation.

MEDICAL PROBLEMS: "I'm doomed to suffer"; feeling self-pity; giving up on medication and treatment; not seeking a second opinion; not exploring all options.

LOSSES: "Life isn't worth living without the person or thing that is gone"; feeling despair; suicide attempt; isolation.

Elicit verbal examples of 'stars' or positive thoughts, feelings and actions for each situation, such as:

ABUSIVE RELATIONSHIPS: "I deserve love and respect"; feeling worthwhile; telling professionals or the police; seeking a safe shelter.

MENTAL ILLNESS: "I have a treatable condition; I can have a satisfying life"; feeling hopeful; continuing to seek effective medication and therapy.

SUBSTANCE ABUSE: "I'll find clean and sober pleasures"; feeling natural 'highs' through friendships with recovering people, meetings, hobbies, helping others; staying sober.

FAMILY OF PARTNER PROBLEMS: "We can work out our problems"; feeling love despite disappointment and realizing conflict is common; trying communication, compromise; seeking professional help.

FINANCIAL PROBLEMS: "I will meet my needs"; feeling empowered; applying for financial assistance or seeking employment; obtaining credit counseling; exploring social services for food, housing and utility assistance.

MEDICAL PROBLEMS: "I can seek relief"; feeling self-nurturing; exploring treatment options with doctors; reading about alternatives; communicating with others who are fighting the disease.

LOSSES: "I'll find strength to go on; my life has purpose"; feeling loss without giving up; learning about the stages of grief; joining a support group; getting therapy.

FACILITATOR'S INFORMATION
Things To Be Desired

AGE	DIFFICULTY	PAGES
A & T	2	2

PURPOSE To personalize concepts of self-acceptance, faith, peace and love.

MATERIALS Board, marker, pencils, 'THINGS TO BE DESIRED' WORKSHEET, page 129.

ATTENTION GRABBER Volunteer writes "Things to be desired"… on board and lists as peers brainstorm things they desire.

ACTIVITY Volunteer writes 'DESIDERATA' on board. Explain the word is Latin for 'things to be desired'. Distribute worksheet with 'DESIDERATA' by Max Ehrmann and related questions. Read the poem in unison a few times. Then people take turns selecting and writing one sentence on board and sharing its relevance to their lives.

FOLLOW-UP Individuals complete worksheet questions. Whole group then discusses answers.

VARIATION I. Facilitator or volunteers ask worksheet questions while participants answer orally.

II. Divide into dyads. Each questions partner, records responses, then 'presents' partner to the group and encourages feedback. "This is Mark and his answer to number one is…"

THINGS TO BE DESIRED

WORKSHEET

DESIDERATA

GO PLACIDLY AMID THE NOISE & HASTE, & REMEMBER WHAT PEACE THERE MAY BE IN SILENCE. AS FAR AS POSSIBLE WITHOUT surrender be on good terms with all persons. Speak your truth quietly and clearly; and listen to others, even the dull & ignorant; they too have their story. ❧ Avoid loud & aggressive persons, they are vexatious to the spirit. If you compare yourself with others, you may become bitter or vain, for always there will be greater & lesser persons than yourself. Enjoy your achievements as well as your plans. ❧ Keep interested in your own career, however humble; it is a real possession in the changing fortunes of time. Exercise caution in your business affairs; for the world is full of trickery. But let this not blind you to what virtue there is; many persons strive for high ideals; and everywhere life is full of heroism ❧ Be yourself. Especially, do not feign affection. Neither be cynical about love; for in the face of all aridity & disenchantment it is perennial as the grass. ❧ Take kindly the counsel of the years, gracefully surrendering the things of youth. Nurture strength of spirit to shield you in sudden misfortune. But do not distress yourself with imaginings. Many fears are born of fatigue & loneliness. Beyond a wholesome discipline, be gentle with yourself. ❧ You are a child of the universe, no less than the trees & the stars; you have a right to be here. And whether or not it is clear to you, no doubt the universe is unfolding as it should. ❧ Therefore be at peace with God, whatever you conceive Him to be, and whatever your labors & aspirations, in the noisy confusion of life keep peace with your soul. ❧ With all its sham, drudgery & broken dreams, it is still a beautiful world. Be cheerful. Strive to be happy. ❧ ❧

Max Ehrmann

According to the author:

1. What happens if we compare ourselves to others and why? _____

2. Give two examples of heroism you have portrayed or witnessed. _____

3. Tell at least two ways you can "be yourself" _____

4. Give a current or recent example of distressing yourself with "imaginings" _____

5. In what two ways do you achieve a "wholesome discipline" in your life? _____

6. Tell at least two ways you can "be gentle with yourself". _____

7. How does "And whether or not it is clear to you, no doubt the universe is unfolding as it should" relate to your life right now? _____

8. How do you "nurture strength of spirit" and "keep peace with your soul"? _____

9. Despite your disappointments, how is yours " still a beautiful world"? _____

10. In your opinion, what is this poem's most meaningful message? _____

WORDS OF WISDOM

AGE	DIFFICULTY	PAGES
A & T	2	2

PURPOSE

Apply wisdom to our own lives.

MATERIALS

Board, marker, basket with eggs, container for CUT-UPS, 'WORDS OF WISDOM' CUT-UPS, page 131.
Use intact page of quotes for all to read.
Use one page of CUT-UPS for the guessing game.

ATTENTION GRABBER

Ask, "What are Words of Wisdom?" and ask people to share their favorites.
Show a basket of eggs and ask what it brings to mind ("Don't put all your eggs in one basket.")
Discuss.

ACTIVITY

Distribute 'WORDS OF WISDOM' page intact and take turns reading quotes. Instruct people to familiarize themselves with them, as they will be turning their paper face down for the game.
First person comes to front of room, picks a CUT-UP and acts out as in Charades, draws on board or uses blanks for letters as in Wheel of Fortune or Hang Man. Whoever guesses must interpret the proverb and tell how it applies to him/her. If guesser already had a turn, s/he picks someone else.

FOLLOW-UP

I. Each states which is most relevant to her/him and why.

II. People share their own words of wisdom or compose new ones in pairs or teams.

VARIATION

Have props such as salt, milk, dirt, a rug, umbrella, lemons and lemonade. One group per prop could be facilitated. Example: Use lemons and lemonade as Attention Grabbers. ("If life gives you lemons, make lemonade.") Each person writes and then shares a time s/he turned a seemingly unfavorable situation to his/her advantage. After sharing, each gets a glass of lemonade.

Similar groups can incorporate:
"Take it with a grain of salt."
"Don't cry over spilt milk."
"Don't sweep it under the rug."
"Don't get wet until it rains."

WORDS OF WISDOM

1 Honesty is the best policy.	**2** Haste makes waste.	**3** It does not matter whether you win or lose; it is how you play the game.
4 People who live in glass houses should not throw stones.	**5** Go the extra mile.	**6** When the going gets tough, the tough get going.
7 Do the thing you fear, and the death of fear is certain.	**8** You catch more flies with honey than you do with vinegar.	**9** Forgive and forget.
10 Live and let live.	**11** Look before you leap.	**12** Early to bed, early to rise, makes a man healthy, wealthy and wise.
13 All that glitters is not gold.	**14** You get what you expect.	**15** Remember the turtle and the hare.
16 Loose lips sink ships.	**17** Every cloud has a silver lining.	**18** A stitch in time saves nine.
19 Get it off your chest.	**20** Birds of a feather flock together.	**21** Live one day at a time.
22 The grass always looks greener on the other side.	**23** The further down the road you go the less likely you are to turn back.	**24** Change the doing to change the viewing.

MENTAL HEALTH & SOBRIETY

MENTAL HEALTH/ SOBRIETY views mental illness and addiction as potentially independent conditions occurring concurrently. What exacerbates one usually worsens the other; what improves one usually helps the other; treatment techniques compliment each other. Participants experience the benefits of support groups, recognize stages of recovery, and avoid allowing their diagnoses to define or consume them.

ACTIVITY	PAGE NUMBERS	AGE	LEVEL OF DIFFICULTY	PAGES
Group Concepts and Benefits	135 - 137	A & T	2	3
Group Roles: Who Am I?	138 - 140	A & T	2	3
Name that Stage	141 - 143	A & T	2	3
Perspectives	144 - 147	A & T	2	4
Rash of Destruction	148 - 150	A & T	2	3

AGES:
ALL = ALL ages, 8 or 9 through adults
YP = YOUNG PEOPLE, ages 8 or 9 through 17
T = TEENS, ages 13 through 17
A & T = ADULTS and TEENS, ages 13 and older
A = ADULTS, ages 18 and older
* = SPECIFIC PAGES expressly for this population.

LEVEL OF DIFFICULTY:
1 = EASIER - basic language; minimal reading and writing
2 = MODERATE - introduces new terminology; incorporates life experiences
3 = MORE DIFFICULT - requires some prior knowledge or introduction of new information; promotes peer teaching

PAGES: The total number of pages related to the activity, including FACILITATOR'S INFORMATION and all accompanying pages.

FACILITATOR'S INFORMATION
GROUP CONCEPTS & BENEFITS

*To learn more about groups, consult <u>The Theory and Practice of Group Psychotherapy</u> by I. D. Yalom, (1985), New York: Basic Books.

AGE	DIFFICULTY	PAGES
A & T	2	3

PURPOSE

To recognize value and actively achieve benefits from group participation

MATERIALS

Board, marker, container for CUT-UPS, a single twig or coffee swizzle stick and a handful of twigs or swizzle sticks bundled together with a rubber band, envelope or box, pencils, 'GROUP CONCEPTS & BENEFITS' CUT-UPS, page 136, and MATCHING, page 137. (Optional) prizes or play money (SKILLS BILLS, pages 277, 278).

ATTENTION GRABBER

Ask a volunteer to break or bend the single twig or swizzle stick, then to attempt to break or bend the bundle. Ask, "Why is it harder to break the bundle?" (Because they're stronger together than alone.) Ask, "How does this relate to us?" Elicit ideas about strengthening and helping each other through educational, therapeutic and support groups.

ACTIVITY

Explain, "We are going to play a Matching Game but first we must understand some terms." Participants take turns writing concepts and benefits, (from cut-ups), on board and eliciting people's experiences. Example: " Who received feedback in a group and how did it help?"

After all terms have been discussed, play the Matching Game: 'Game Show Host' uses the MATCHING page and lists benefits, numbers 1 through 14, on board. Divide into two teams. Starting with "a" and ending with "n", 'Host' reads definitions as teams take turns guessing the matching term. Members confer, but only one 'final answer' is allowed. If one team answers incorrectly, the other team tries.

ANSWER KEY: 1-j, 2-f, 3-l, 4-a, 5-h, 6-b, 7-c, 8-d, 9-g, 10-k, 11-i, 12-e, 13-n, 14-m.
BONUS QUESTIONS: 'Host' asks questions at bottom of MATCHING page. Teams accrue points or play money for correct answers; team with the most wins.

FOLLOW-UP

I. Each identifies at least one benefit s/he experienced during today's group.

II. Discuss advantages of specific groups including Grief and Loss, Alcoholics Anonymous, Narcotics Anonymous, Dual Diagnosis Anonymous, Overeaters Anonymous, Co-dependents Anonymous, Emotions Anonymous, Adult Children of Alcoholics, Gamblers Anonymous, Sex Addicts Anonymous, National Alliance For The Mentally Ill, groups for victims of abuse, people dealing with physical diseases, injuries, and others. If possible, display pamphlets and/or ask volunteers to visit or contact groups and organizations and present information to peers.

III. As a group, visit open meetings then discuss benefits. On an in-patient unit, participants may start their own support group or community representatives may meet at the hospital or institution, for a presentation , or on a weekly basis.

VARIATION

I. After group concepts and benefits have been discussed, teams go to separate corners or rooms. Allow about fifteen minutes to prepare MATCHING page answers in advance, then play game as noted in ACTIVITY , using their 'cheat sheets'.

II. After group concepts and benefits have been discussed, teams go to separate rooms or corners. Allow about fifteen minutes to complete MATCHING page answers. Then reconvene and read answers aloud. Team with the most correct answers to numbers 1 through 14 wins the MATCHING contest; team with the most detailed responses to the questions at bottom of the page wins the BONUS contest.

GROUP CONCEPTS & BENEFITS

1 Microcosm – group is a small segment of the outside world; how we think, feel and/or act here relates to our everyday behavior.	**2** Interpersonal Learning – people learn from each other by sharing ideas.	**3** Role-playing – allows for the practice of skills.	**4** Comradeship – is working together on a project and going through an experience together which can lead to friendships and/or support.
5 Peer pressures – can be positive or negative.	**6** Catharsis – release pent-up emotion.	**7** Universality – others have the same problem.	**8** Altruism – by helping others, I help myself.
9 Cohesiveness – members stick together, support each other.	**10** Feedback – listening to others' opinions.	**11** Insight – learning about myself.	**12** Tolerance – acceptance, not judging or labeling others.
13 Reality testing – comparing my beliefs with others.	**14** Trying out new behaviors – 'practicing' on peers.	**15** Re-creating family dynamics – reacting differently to parent figures; sibling rivalry (may be resolved).	**16** Instill hope – others have survived, maybe I can too.
17 Share information – what is helpful to one person may benefit me.	**18** Develop socializing techniques – before and/or after group, over lunch or coffee, we talk, laugh, joke.	**19** Imitation – a more advanced peer takes meds, goes to therapy, has a hobby; I may decide to try these.	**20** Roles – members' behaviors which may be helpful or hurtful to themselves, others, and to group as a whole.

GROUP CONCEPTS & BENEFITS

MATTCHING

_____ 1. Catharsis   a. sticking together

_____ 2. Universality   b. getting to know myself

_____ 3. Altruism   c. acceptance

_____ 4. Cohesiveness   d. compare beliefs or perceptions

_____ 5. Feedback   e. 'practice' new ways to act

_____ 6. Insight   f. others have my problem

_____ 7. Tolerance   g. they improved, so I can too

_____ 8. Reality testing   h. getting other's opinions

_____ 9. Hope   i. copy behaviors I admire

_____ 10. Sharing information   j. release of emotions

_____ 11. Imitation   k. learning from others

_____ 12. Try out behaviors   l. helping others

_____ 13. Family dynamics   m. coffee breaks, lunchtime – time for talking and laughing

_____ 14. Socializing   n. sibling rivalry, rebellion against parents relived through relationships with group members and/or leaders

Name five benefits you have received and give specific examples.

What is the most important benefit to you? (give reasons)

What new behaviors do you want to practice with group members and in daily life? (give reasons)

Give an example of how you helped someone and how it benefited you.

FACILITATOR'S INFORMATION
GROUP ROLES: WHO AM I?

* To learn more about groups, consult <u>The Theory and Practice of Group Psychotherapy</u>
  by I. D. Yalom, (1985), New York: Basic Books.

AGE	DIFFICULTY	PAGES
A & T	2	3

PURPOSE

To recognize and choose positive roles.

MATERIALS

Board, marker, container for CUT-UPS, pencils,
'GROUP ROLES: WHO AM I?' CUT-UPS, page 139,
MATCHING, page 140.
(Optional) prizes or play money (SKILLS BILLS, pages 277, 278).

ATTENTION GRABBER

Volunteer, coached before group, tells jokes, makes funny faces, and snickers as facilitator tries to start group session. Ask, "How is s/he acting?" (silly). "What do we call people like this, especially in school?" (class clown).

ACTIVITY

Explain, "We are going to play a Matching Game but first we must learn the roles people play in groups. Who has known a class clown? Why does the person over-use humor?" (to seek attention and reduce nervousness). " What topics usually make people giggle?" (sex and uncomfortable subjects). Participants take turns writing roles, (from cut-ups), on board and eliciting peers' interpretations of the definitions. Example: "What does the Harmonizer do?"After all roles have been defined, play the Matching Game. 'Game Show Host' uses the MATCHING page and lists roles, numbers 1 through 16, on board. Starting with "a" and ending with "p" 'Host' reads definitions as teams take turns guessing the matching role. Members confer, but only one 'final answer' is allowed. If one team answers incorrectly, the other team tries.
ANSWER KEY:1-j, 2-p, 3-a, 4-g, 5-c, 6-b, 7-l, 8-d, 9-h, 10-e, 11-m, 12-n, 13-o, 14-f, 15-i, 16-k.
BONUS QUESTIONS: 'Host' asks the questions at the bottom of MATCHING page. One team must answer the first two questions. Each member names a role s/he usually assumes, giving examples of words and actions. If someone doesn't know, teammates may share their perceptions of that person's role and behavior. Team gets a point or play money for each role they describe. Other team must answer the third question. Each member names a role s/he would like to assume and shares why. Teammates may rescue the person who doesn't know by suggesting a positive role with behavioral description. The last question is in two parts: one team lists and describes helpful roles; other team lists and describes hurtful roles. Teams accrue points or play money for correct answers; team with the most wins.

FOLLOW-UP

I. Discuss what motivates people to assume specific roles, particularly in dysfunctional families. Examples: Harmonizer may have witnessed domestic violence and fears conflict; Aggressor may have been verbally or physically abused; Scapegoat may be accustomed to accepting blame.Ask, "Do people generally play out their group roles in the 'outside world' or in life?" Encourage discussion, debate and examples.

II. With high-functioning people, pass container of CUT-UPS. Each selects a role with definition (from CUT-UP page). Discuss a topic, (current events, politics, television, music, etc.), for five minutes while each portrays his/her role. Then participants guess which roles peers were playing.

VARIATION

I. After roles have been discussed, teams go to separate rooms or corners. Allow about fifteen minutes to prepare MATCHING page answers in advance. Then play game as noted in ACTIVITY, using their 'cheat sheets'.

II. Teams go to separate rooms or corners. Allow about fifteen minutes to prepare MATCHING page answers. Then reconvene and read answers aloud. Team with the most correct answers to numbers 1 through 16 wins the MATCHING contest; team with the most detailed responses to the questions at bottom of page wins the BONUS contest.

GROUP ROLES: WHO AM I?

1

Harmonizer – *peacemaker.*

2

Questioner – *seeks information; gives constructive criticism.*

3

Deserter – *talks about irrelevant material; is indifferent or disruptive.*

4

Tension reducer – *lightens the mood.*

5

Encourager – *warm, boosts members' self-esteem.*

6

Monopolizer – *tries to control group and does not let others talk.*

7

Clarifier – *restates issues, summarizes.*

8

Opinion giver – *uses own experience to back up opinion or belief.*

9

Initiator – *brings up ideas, brings up topics for discussion and suggests possible solutions.*

10

Listener – *interested facial expression and body language.*

11

Negativist – *pessimistic, argumentative, uncooperative.*

12

Energizer – *pushes group into action.*

13

Aggressor – *hostile, seeks attention, verbally attacks.*

14

Scapegoat – *gets blamed, picked on.*

15

Class clown – *overuses humor.*

16

Mascot – *people take care of this person.*

GROUP ROLES: WHO AM I?

MATCHING

_____ 1. Harmonizer

_____ 2. Questioner

_____ 3. Deserter

_____ 4. Tension Reducer

_____ 5. Encourager

_____ 6. Monopolizer

_____ 7. Clarifier

_____ 8. Opinion giver

_____ 9. Initiator

_____ 10. Listener

_____ 11. Negativist

_____ 12. Energizer

_____ 13. Aggressor

_____ 14. Scapegoat

_____ 15. Clown

_____ 16. Mascot

a. disruptive, changes the subject

b. talks too much

c. warm, boosts esteem

d. tells own beliefs

e. interested facial expression

f. gets picked on

g. lightens the mood

h. new ideas, suggestions

i. over-use of humor

j. peacemaker

k. treated like a pet

l. summarizes clearly

m. pessimistic

n. motivator

o. attacks

p. seeks information

What roles do you usually assume?

Give specific examples of what you said and/or did in each role.

What roles would you like to assume? (give reasons)

Which roles are helpful and hurtful to group? (give reasons)

FACILITATOR'S INFORMATION
Name That Stage

AGE	DIFFICULTY	PAGES
A & T	2	3

PURPOSE

To identify stages of Recovery.

MATERIALS

Board, markers, container for CUT-UPS, EXAMPLE OF WHAT BOARD WILL LOOK LIKE, page 142, and 'NAME THAT STAGE' CUT-UPS, page 143. Paper, crayons and pencils for the variation. Instant camera, if photographs are allowed.

ATTENTION GRABBER

Volunteer draws five sections using vertical lines on board [for BEFORE BOTTOM (BB), BOTTOM (B), ON THE FENCE (F), COMMITMENT (C), and LIFE GOES ON (LGO)] and labels each with:

BB	B	F	C	LGO

Volunteer draws (from example on CUT-UP) the bottom (X) and asks group what this represents – the person draws in the "B" section.

ACTIVITY

Discuss hitting bottom – put key words and/or phrases under 'B' on board.
   (BOTTOM: lose job, divorce, poor health, suicidal).
Discuss, label and note key words for 'BEFORE BOTTOM' (BB), (partying, arguing, relationship and/or work problems).
Volunteer draws (from example on CUT-UP provided) a fence under 'F'.
Group guesses the word – discusses being 'ON THE FENCE' or ambivalence about sobriety and/or recovery from mental illness.
For COMMITMENT – draw the appropriate number of blanks for the letters and have people guess the word. Do same for 'LIFE GOES ON (LGO)'.
   People may copy symbols on board also.
Discuss what actions people take when committed to recovery and during the 'LIFE GOES ON' stage where recovery program is integrated into other aspects of life – family, school and/or work.
Put CUT-UPS in container and pass around.
Take turns reading behavioral statements while peers guess the stage. People may disagree with the answers and more than one stage may apply to a statement. Answers are coded by letter in the bottom right corners of CUT-UPS.
Validate and accept any sensible answers.

FOLLOW-UP

Participants place their photo and/or initials on board in their current stage and receive suggestions on moving to the next stage.

VARIATION

People draw what they were, are and will be doing in each stage and share their drawings.

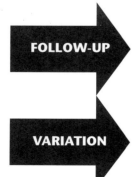

141

Name That Stage

#1. Each column begins with symbols and/or labels and peers guess the words/meanings.
#2. They brainstorm components of each stage while a peer lists them.
#3. They place photos or initials on stage they are in.

	BB Before Bottom 〰	B Bottom ⌐⌐	F Fence ▦	C Commitment ◯◯	LGO Life Goes On 𝓮𝓮𝓮
Labels #1					
Labels #2	a. Partying b. Denial c. Relationship problems d. Work problems e. Hangovers f. Highs and lows g. Some health problems	a. Job Loss b. Divorce c. Depression d. Suicidal or homicidal e. Poor health f. Jail g. Lost driver's license h. Refuses therapy or medications	a. Not sure about wanting to quit b. Glamorizes the 'good old days' c. Doesn't want to give up old friends. d. Might go to a few meetings. e. Might see a psychiatrist or therapist. f. Takes medicine sometimes. g. Admits a problem.	a. Meetings daily at first. b. Contacts sponsor daily at first. c. Completes the steps. d. Detaches from old friends. e. Gets rid of all drinking, drug supplies and contacts. f. Tells medical doctor and dentist so no addictive medicines are prescribed. g. No new romantic entanglements. h. Takes prescribed medicines regularly. i. Anger management class, if necessary	a. Education (start with one class at a time.) b. Employment (avoid excessive stress at first.) c. Relationships (with sober people and proceed slowly.) d. Hobbies, clubs, sports are very important.
Labels #3	3. Photos or initials of members in their current stage. Each tells why s/he placed self there and states how s/he can move into the next stage.				3. NOTE: If someone places her/himself in a more advanced stage, encourage peers to ask questions and hopefully the person will change to a more realistic stage.

142

NAME THAT STAGE

BB	B	F	C	LGO

1 Cutting wrist. B	2 Tells true feelings to counselor. C	3 Skips medicine a few times a week. F	4 Gets drunk. BB or B	5 Involved in a serious romance. LGO
6 Signs up for full schedule of classes. LGO	7 If a situation cannot be changed, learns to change own thoughts and behavior related to it. C	8 Drinks and/or uses less often – only on special occasions. F	9 Joins a sports team or club. LGO	10 Sometimes expresses honest feelings about anger or hurt feelings and sometimes stuffs the feeling. F
11 Uses coping skills (talking, meditation, exercise) once in a while. F	12 Tells doctor if medicine has side effects instead of just stopping on his/her own. C	13 Threatens suicide or homicide. B	14 Takes a volunteer or paid job. LGO	15 Takes medicine as prescribed. C
16 Overdoses. B	17 Asks for information about sobriety or medicine or therapy. F	18 Asks for help immediately if has urge to drink, use and/or hurt self. C	19 Uses street drugs. BB or B	20 Denies having an addiction or emotional problem. BB or B

143

FACILITATOR'S INFORMATION
PERSPECTIVES

AGE	DIFFICULTY	PAGES
A & T	2	4

PLEASE NOTE: **This activity will probably require two sessions, approximately fifty minutes each.**

PURPOSE

To view mental illness and/or substance abuse in proper perspective, neither denying its existence nor defining self with it. To identify disease concepts, grief and loss stages related to illness while developing hope and striving toward normalization (the least restrictive and highest quality of life possible).

MATERIALS

Board, marker, container for CUT-UPS, hospital gown, bedpan, pitcher, or emesis basin, 'PERSPECTIVES' CUT-UPS, page 145, WORKSHEET, page 146 , SUGGESTED ANSWERS and CONCEPTS, page 147.

ATTENTION GRABBER

Volunteer walks in wearing hospital gown and carrying an emesis basin, pitcher or bedpan. Ask participants, "What do we know about this person?" (S/he is ill.) Volunteer writes "DISEASE" on board. Brainstorm what comes to mind when they hear this word.

ACTIVITY

1. Volunteers write definitions on board: DISEASE = lack of ease, SIGNS = noticed by others, and SYMPTOMS = reported by the patient. Take turns sitting in the 'spotlight seat' and sharing how their conditions caused lack of ease, signs their family and/or friends observed and symptoms they felt at the time they were diagnosed or sought treatment.
2. Three volunteers, coached before group, leave the room then re-enter, shake everyone's hand and state, "I'm a Bipolar ", "I'm a Schizophrenic", "I'm a Depressive". Ask participants, "What do you think about people presenting themselves this way?" Responses may vary; hopefully someone will comment, "At least they're not in denial!" Ask, "What is wrong with defining yourself as your diagnosis?" Elicit that there is much more to a person than his/her disease.
3. Ask, "What happens to a person with poor eyesight?" Elicit that as long as they wear the glasses (or contacts, or have laser surgery) they can lead a fairly normal life. Ask about people with Diabetes. Elicit that with insulin and proper diet they can lead a fairly normal life. Compare the chronic nature of these conditions to mental and/or substance abuse problems: medications, therapy and lifestyle changes facilitate productive and enjoyable lives.
4. Brainstorm names and accomplishments of past or present famous people who had mental illness and/or substance abuse problems. Elicit that genius and talent often coexist with these conditions.
5. Divide into six dyads or teams who choose a topic, (Denial, Anger, Bargaining, Depression, Acceptance, Extremes), receive related questions from CUT-UP page, and go to separate areas of room to write or plan answers. Then the participants reunite. Teams take turns sitting in front of the group, writing topic on board, sharing their responses and eliciting feedback from 'audience'.

FOLLOW-UP

Distribute WORKSHEET, page 146. Individuals, dyads or teams answer questions then discuss and share responses. Facilitators should review and retain 'SUGGESTED ANSWERS AND CONCEPTS TO INCLUDE', page 147, as possible responses to elicit from participants, but accept any plausible answers.

VARIATION

'Talk Show Host' calls individuals to the 'spotlight seat' where they answer different questions.

Perspectives

DENIAL
1. Tell about a time you denied your illness to yourself and others.
2. How did denial prevent or delay getting treatment?
3. Why do people often deny mental illness and/or substance abuse?
4. Did or do any family members and/or friends deny your disease? How does this make you feel?

ANGER
1. Tell about a time you were angry about your disease.
2. How did anger affect your progress?
3. Who else was or is angry about your illness and how does this affect your recovery?

BARGAINING
1. Tell about a time you tried to bargain with your Higher Power or someone else about your disease. Examples: "If you give me one more chance, I'll never drink, use, cut or blow-up again". "If you let me drink socially, I'll never get drunk".
2. What usually happens when we make these kinds of 'deals'?
3. How does bargaining prevent or delay getting treatment?

DEPRESSION
1. Tell a time you were depressed about your illness.
2. How do low energy and negative thinking affect your willingness to get treatment?
3. Who else seems depressed about your illness and how does this affect you?

ACCEPTANCE
1. How does facing the facts affect your recovery?
2. What are the components of treatment for mental illness? (Discuss benefits of medicine, productive activity and therapy.)
3. What are the components of treatment for substance abuse? (Discuss benefits of step work, support groups, individual therapy, lifestyle changes and possibly medicine to help with concurrent mental illness or to decrease cravings.)

EXTREMES
1. Describe a person who goes to extremes about his/her illness. (Examples: decides s/he is totally incapacitated by disease and will never work, love, or enjoy life again; talks too much about it; researches the diagnosis too much and has exaggerated symptoms).
2. How does over-emphasis on illness affect quality of life? What are some secondary gains some people seek? (Discuss attention; sympathy; avoiding work, school, productive activity; and isolation.)
3. How can the 'extremist' achieve a balance? (Discuss value of volunteer work, community activities, sports, hobbies and other ways to achieve an identity.)

Perspectives

1. How has your condition affected your life physically, intellectually, emotionally, socially, spiritually, and financially? Have you suffered legal consequences? _____
_____
_____

2. How can you improve your life physically, intellectually, emotionally, spiritually and financially, with proper treatment? _____
_____
_____

3. Discuss denial, anger, bargaining, depression and acceptance. Which stage applies to you right now and why? _____
_____
_____

4. Describe a person who over-emphasizes his/her illness: What does s/he talk mostly about? What activities are avoided? _____
_____
_____

5. Why do some people enjoy being 'sick'? _____
_____
_____

6. What is the difference between accepting an illness and exaggerating its effect on life? _____
_____
_____

7. When is it necessary to place other aspects of life 'on hold' and devote full attention to your illness? _____
_____
_____

8. Give examples of 'healthy selfishness' related to recovery from mental illness and substance abuse.
_____
_____

9. What percent of your self-concept involves your mental illness and/or substance abuse now? How do you see this changing over the next six months? Year? Five years? _____
_____
_____

10. Describe at least three strengths you have developed through facing the challenges of your illness. _____
_____

PERSPECTIVES

SUGGESTED ANSWERS and CONCEPTS TO INCLUDE

1. Mental illness often affects physical health through weight gain or loss, poor grooming hygiene, insomnia or excessive sleep, side effects of medications, self-harm and suicide. Emotional effects include mood swings, 'numbness', lack of pleasure, anger and/or homicidal feelings. Intellectual function temporarily declines due to lack of interest and energy and preoccupation with troublesome thoughts and/or hallucinations. Social withdrawal usually occurs. Spirituality suffers from loss of faith and hope or preoccupation with guilt and fear. Finances decrease when people can't work or from over-spending during a manic 'high'. Anger problems often lead to assault and battery charges. Substance abuse also includes damage to liver and other organs, emotional roller coaster (highs under the influence and lows without the substance), poor attention span and/or concentration, potential brain damage, fraternizing with potentially dangerous drug dealers and gangs. Additional legal consequences may result from being under the influence, possession, sales, or from stealing to get money for drugs and/or alcohol.

2. Answers include improvement in areas mentioned in #1.

3. These are addressed in the activity through questions on CUT-UP page 145 Stages will vary.

4. The person talks excessively about the symptoms, medications, side effects, and enjoys telling 'horror stories' about self-harm and/or suicide or bragging about anger outbursts and/or intimidation. S/he lacks interest in other people, hobbies, current events, career, and often avoids school, work and/or volunteering. S/he misses out on productive and enjoyable activities. The substance abuser tells 'war stories', often glamorizing 'the good old days'.

5. Secondary gains include attention, sympathy, lowered expectations from self or others, avoiding responsibilities for family, school or work. Disability pay is a necessary blessing for *most* people but *some* receive benefits when they *are* able to work. Proving their severity of impairment prevents wellness activities.

6. Accepting illness involves compliance with treatment and functioning within your capabilities and limitations. If your condition prohibits paid work, then volunteer, join a club, take a class, or develop a talent. Exaggeration encompasses withdrawal from life's responsibilities and rewards.

7. During the initial stages or a flare-up of mental illness, crisis intervention and symptom relief take priority. Additional challenges are not recommended. People struggling with early recovery from substance abuse or at risk for relapse may need to engage one hundred percent in meetings and/or step work.

8. Healthy selfishness is putting recovery first. Examples include refusing a request to help someone if it conflicts with a therapy appointment, support group meeting or saying no to a family gathering where liquor will be served if exposure could trigger cravings.

9. Percents appropriated to illness are usually higher during acute exacerbation or upon initial diagnosis. With time and treatment, other qualities predominate. Self-concept should focus on interests, abilities, traits such as kindness, sense of humor, diligence and family and community work-related roles.

10. Adversity promotes perseverance, compassion, wisdom, tolerance, faith and other attributes.

FACILITATOR'S INFORMATION
RASH OF DESTRUCTION

AGE	DIFFICULTY	PAGES
A & T	2	3

PURPOSE

To avoid hazardous substances, situations and thoughts.

MATERIALS

Board, red marker, container for CUT-UPS, tape, red make-up, 'NURSE HIVES' and 'DR. RASH' name tags, 'ALLERGIC TO' and 'ANTIDOTE' labels, page 150, and 'RASH OF DESTRUCTION' WORKSHEET, page 149. If available, stethoscope and/or white lab jacket.

ATTENTION GRABBER

Two volunteers prepare and practice before group. 'Doctor Rash' or 'Nurse Hives' wears name- tag, (and if available has stethoscope/ white lab jacket). Patient applies make-up: red dots on face and/or arms. They role-play this scenario: 'Doctor' or 'nurse' asks, "Do you have any allergies"? Patient replies, "Yes, alcohol. Whenever I drink, I break out in a rash of destruction". NOTE: If make-up is unavailable, patient draws face and/or body on board with red dots all over.

ACTIVITY

Ask if anyone has allergies or knows someone with them. Encourage brief discussion. Volunteer writes definitions on board:
   ALLERGY: hypersensitivity to a substance.
   ALLERGEN: substance that causes the unpleasant or dangerous reaction.
   ANTIDOTE: whatever neutralizes the dangerous substance.

Ask for examples of 'rash of destruction' resulting from drinking (in a person with this sensitivity). Responses may include fights, assault and/or battery charges, domestic violence, felony drunk driving, health problems, job loss, divorce, possibly suicide or homicide as both are more likely when under the influence.

Brainstorm or list on board other 'allergens'. Responses include street drugs, addictive prescription medicines, degrading people and relationships, thoughts that glamorize substances, self harm and/or violence.

Distribute allergy and antidote labels and questions. Divide into dyads. Take turns asking and recording partner's responses. Explain that answers should relate to topics discussed. People should *not* be discussing allergens such as pollen, cat hair or penicillin! Fill out allergy and antidote labels for partners. Then all participants reconvene and dyads go to 'spotlight seats' and present partners responses and receive peer feedback and suggestions. "This is Mary and she is allergic to_____." Those who are willing may wear their labels for the rest of group and/or day. They should keep and display them on their walls, mirrors, coffee cups or other prominent place.

FOLLOW-UP

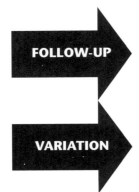

Each shares one insight developed about self and partner. A few days or a week later, discuss how their daily plans for avoidance and substitution are working.

VARIATION

People answer own questions and share responses with group.

RASH OF DESTRUCTION

1. What are you allergic to? _____
_____
_____

2. What happens if you are exposed to your allergen(s)? _____
_____
_____

3. How can you avoid contact with your allergen(s)? _____
_____
_____

4. Does the amount of the substance matter? (answer is **NO** because a small amount can be deadly).
_____
_____

5. What is/are the antidote(s)? (answers may include support group meetings, sponsors, step work, clean, sober fun for substance abuse; medication, therapy, talking about thoughts and feelings, coping skills for negative and/or self-harm thoughts. For severe suicidal or homicidal urges or relapse binge, calling 911 or entering a hospital or residential treatment program is essential.)
_____
_____

6. Describe a daily or weekly plan for avoiding your allergen(s). Tell **who** you'll be with, **what** you'll do, **where** you'll go, **when** and **how** you'll use your antidote(s). _____
_____
_____

7. Allergens often seem to give pleasure (drugs and alcohol) or meet a need (love and belonging through an abusive relationship, or getting rid of emotional pain by cutting on self). Describe your substitution(s). Tell **who, what, where, when** and **how** you'll use safe and healthy replacements.
_____
_____

RASH OF DESTRUCTION

NURSE HIVES

DR. RASH

ANTIDOTE:

_____

ALLERGIC TO:

_____

PROBLEM SOLVING

PROBLEM SOLVING meets people at 'crossroads', crises, and less monumental decision-making points in life. They brainstorm possibilities, evaluate options and ultimately make independent but educated decisions.

ACTIVITY	PAGE NUMBERS	AGE	LEVEL OF DIFFICULTY	PAGES
Fork in the Road	153 - 154	A & T	2	2
Get a Grip	155	ALL	1	1
Get the Points	156 - 157	ALL	1	2
Pros and Cons	158 - 159	A & T	1	2

LEGEND

AGES:
ALL = ALL ages, 8 or 9 through adults
YP = YOUNG PEOPLE, ages 8 or 9 through 17
T = TEENS, ages 13 through 17
A & T = ADULTS and TEENS, ages 13 and older
A = ADULTS, ages 18 and older
* = SPECIFIC PAGES expressly for this population.

LEVEL OF DIFFICULTY:
1 = EASIER - basic language; minimal reading and writing
2 = MODERATE - introduces new terminology; incorporates life experiences
3 = MORE DIFFICULT - requires some prior knowledge or introduction of new information; promotes peer teaching

PAGES:
The total number of pages related to the activity, including FACILITATOR'S INFORMATION and all accompanying pages.

FORK IN THE ROAD

AGE	DIFFICULTY	PAGES
A & T	2	2

PURPOSE

To practice decision-making, identify opportunities and consider advantages of new challenges.

MATERIALS

Board, marker, pencils, plastic fork, and 'FORK IN THE ROAD' WORKSHEET, page 154.

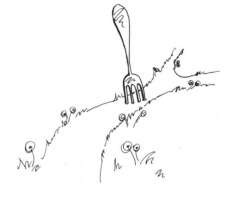

ATTENTION GRABBER

Volunteer shows fork, then draws a 'Y' on board and asks "What is this?". S/he elicits concept of 'fork in the road' and asks peers, "What does it mean to face a fork in the road?" Discuss deciding between two choices.

ACTIVITY

Distribute worksheet with "The Road Not Taken" by Robert Frost and related questions. Read poem in unison a few times and discuss people's interpretations. Allow about fifteen minutes for participants to write answers to worksheet questions. Discuss their responses.

FOLLOW-UP

Each shares at least one insight developed during the activity.

VARIATION

I. Facilitator or volunteers ask worksheet questions while participants answer orally.

II. Divide into dyads. Each asks partner the questions, records responses, then 'presents' partner to the group and encourages feedback. "This is Cindy. She faced two choices when…"

Fork In The Road

The Road Not Taken

Two roads diverged in a yellow wood,
And sorry I could not travel both
And be one traveler, long I stood
And looked down one as far as I could
To where it bent in the undergrowth;

Then took the other, as just as fair,
And having perhaps the better claim,
Because it was grassy and wanted wear;
Though as for that the passing there
Had worn them really about the same,

And both that morning equally lay
In leaves no step had trodden black.
Oh, I kept the first for another day!
Yet knowing how way leads on to way,
I doubted if I should ever come back.

I shall be telling this with a sigh
Somewhere ages and ages hence:
Two roads diverged in a wood, and I —
I took the one less traveled by,
And that has made all the difference.

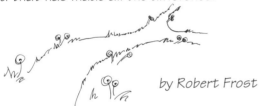

by Robert Frost

* From "The Road Not Taken" from THE POETRY OF ROBERT FROST
edited by Edward Connery Lathem, ©1969 by Henry Holt & Co., LLC.
Reprinted by permission of Henry Holt & Co., LLC.

1. When did you face two choices?

2. Which did you choose and why?

3. What was the outcome?

4. What does it mean to take the "road less traveled by"?

5. When did you take an unfamiliar 'road'?

6. What were the results?

7. Give three examples of unfamiliar 'roads' you might take soon. These may involve healthy risks, unpopular decisions, resisting peer pressure and accepting new challenges.

8. How might each choice you noted in #7 "make all the difference"?

9. When is it advisable to take a 'well traveled road'?

10. Describe a 'tried and true' path you are (or need to be) following and its benefits. This may involve your recovery program, doctor's/therapist's recommendations, using coping skills.

GET A GRIP

AGE	DIFFICULTY	PAGES
ALL	1	1

PURPOSE
Identify issues and coping skills.

MATERIALS
Board, marker, grip cloth, jar with lid, blank slips of paper, and pencils.

ATTENTION GRABBER
Volunteer displays jar with tight lid and grip cloth and asks, "What is this used for? What does 'get a grip' mean?"
Volunteer writes 'Get A Grip' on board.

ACTIVITY
Each identifies his/her most troublesome problem and writes it on a slip of paper. Take turns sitting in spotlight seat, putting paper in jar, telling peers the problem, discussing and eliciting suggestions on ways to handle it. Incorporate Problem Solving Steps including identifying the core issue, weighing pros and cons and choosing best alternatives. After discussion, to symbolize process, they use grip cloth, open jar and remove their 'problem.'

FOLLOW-UP
Discuss ways to 'get a grip' on mental illness, substance abuse and other problems <u>individually</u> (medications; changing thoughts, feelings and actions) and through <u>external</u> <u>resources</u> (therapy and support groups).

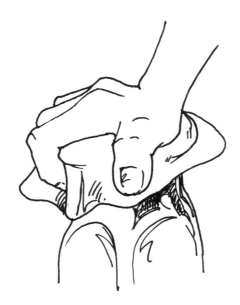

GET THE POINTS

AGE	DIFFICULTY	PAGES
ALL	1	2

PURPOSE

Brainstorm ways to deal with problems.

MATERIALS

Board, marker, pencils, pad of paper for each person, container for CUT-UPS and 'GET THE POINTS' CUT-UPS, page 157.

ATTENTION GRABBER

Volunteer puts 'llll' on board. Ask, "When are these lines used?" (Keeping score.) Pass out pads and pencils and explain they will be tallying points.

ACTIVITY

People anonymously write down current or recent problem situations (or use problems from CUT-UP page or leaders develop their own, relevant to the group's needs.)
Example: "Your partner breaks up with you."
"Someone wants to cheat off you on a test."
"You are tempted to take drugs or drink."
"You feel like hitting someone."
"You got fired."
"You got reprimanded at home, school or work."
"Your parents get a divorce."
"A loved one dies."
Collect in container, which is passed around. First person reads a problem, tells a way to cope and gets one point. Next person tells a second way to cope with the same problem and gets 2 points. Next person tells a third way to cope and gets 3 points and so forth until realistic ways to cope are exhausted or 10 points are earned per problem. Each totals his/her points. Person with the most points wins. Write winner's name on board. Keep score on board showing number of games won by each person. Start fresh with the next problem and new score pad page.

FOLLOW-UP

Discuss which problem and coping skills each found most relevant.

VARIATION

I. Depression Buster Bee, Anger Buster Bee, Craving Buster Bee. All stand in a circle. Each thinks of a way to 'bust' depression, anger, cravings or whatever topic is addressed. If someone repeats one that's been said or cannot state a new 'buster', s/he sits. The last person left standing is the winner. Note: "Get The Points" gives more equal advantages to lower functioning people who can get high points fairly easily and won't be embarrassed by having to sit early or often. If players are equally matched, the 'Buster Bee' is a great alternative.

II. Dyads sit in 'spotlight seats' – one plays 'Dear Abby' and the other reads a problem. 'Abby' suggests ways to cope, then asks the 'audience' for more suggestions. Everyone takes a turn being the 'problem person' and 'Abby'.

GET THE POINTS

1 You have trouble reading and writing.	**2** You drank and want to drive home.	**3** You think you are too fat.	**4** You do not like your looks.
5 Someone tries to start a fight.	**6** You hear voices saying mean things.	**7** People offer you drugs or alcohol.	**8** You want to quit drugs and drinking.
9 You wrecked your parent's or spouse's car or broke something.	**10** Your parents or your children fight.	**11** Someone wants to have sex with you.	**12** A family member gets on your nerves.
13 You hate homework or household chores.	**14** Your parents or spouse always criticize you.	**15** You have trouble sleeping.	**16** You did something wrong and worry about getting caught.
17 Your friends all drink and use and you want to quit.	**18** You lost your job or are expelled from school.	**19** Your parent, spouse or lover hits you.	**20** You have to go to Juvenile Hall (or jail.)
21 You are not good in sports or have no job skills.	**22** Your best friend is ignoring you and hanging around someone else.	**23** You do not get presents from your parents or partner.	**24** You like someone and want friendship (or a relationship.)
25 You feel like cutting, burning or killing yourself.	**26** You want to hurt or kill someone.	**27** Your grades are dropping and/or failing or work performance is declining.	**28** You have little or no money for rent, food or clothes.
29 Someone you love breaks up with you, or you are separated from your parents.	**30** You think people are laughing at you.	**31** Parent, teacher or boss blames you for something you did not do.	**32** Enjoyable activities no longer bring you pleasure.

157

PROS AND CONS

AGE	DIFFICULTY	PAGES
A & T	1	2

PURPOSE

To weigh pros and cons.

MATERIALS

Board, marker, container for CUT-UPS
and 'PROS AND CONS' CUT-UPS, page 159.

ATTENTION GRABBER

Volunteer writes PROS and CONS on board and asks, "What do they mean?"

ACTIVITY

Volunteer selects a CUT-UP, writes question on board and with help of peers, identifies pros and cons. The list can be tailor made to topic you are teaching such as "Should I have just one drink?"

FOLLOW-UP

Each shares a current controversy and his/her pros and cons about it.

VARIATION

People write their <u>own</u> issues on slips of paper with names or anonymously. Then take turns writing these questions, pros, and cons on board.

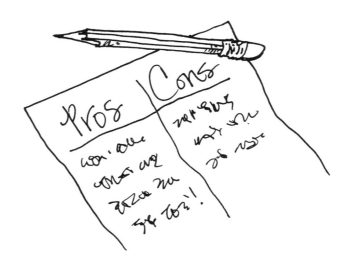

PROS AND CONS

1

Should I return
to school?

2

Should I get
a job?

3

Should I quit
my job?

4

Should I work a
lot of overtime?

5

Should I go on a
blind date?

6

Should I tell the
truth if I know I'll
get in trouble?

7

Should I tell the
truth if someone's
feelings will be
hurt?

8

Should I tell the
truth if it will
make someone
angry?

9

Should I start a
relationship with
_____?

10

Should I end a
relationship with
_____?

11

Should I do
volunteer work?

12

Should I start
vocational
training?

13

Should I
live alone?

14

Should I move in
with
_____?

15

Should I go to
a movie or
restaurant alone?

16

Should I start
an exercise
program?

17

Should I get
a pet?

18

Should I
have sex?

19

Should I drink?

20

Should I
experiment
with drugs?

159

RECOVERY

RECOVERY facilitates understanding of biological, environmental, emotional, legal, financial and family aspects of substance abuse. People consider detriments of drinking and drugs and benefits of sobriety. Slogans help them stay 'on track'.

ACTIVITY	PAGE NUMBERS	AGE	LEVEL OF DIFFICULTY	PAGES
Ace The Quiz	163 - 171	A & T	3	9
Fortune Cookies	172 - 173	A & T	2	2
Save Sandy	174 - 175	A & T	1	2
Tic-Tac-Dope	176 - 181	A & T	3	6
What's a Bar?	182 - 183	A & T	2	2

LEGEND

AGES: ALL = ALL ages, 8 or 9 through adults
YP = YOUNG PEOPLE, ages 8 or 9 through 17
T = TEENS, ages 13 through 17
A & T = ADULTS and TEENS, ages 13 and older
A = ADULTS, ages 18 and older
* = SPECIFIC PAGES expressly for this population.

LEVEL OF   1 = EASIER - basic language; minimal reading and writing
DIFFICULTY: 2 = MODERATE - introduces new terminology; incorporates life experiences
3 = MORE DIFFICULT - requires some prior knowledge or introduction of new information; promotes peer teaching

PAGES: The total number of pages related to the activity, including FACILITATOR'S INFORMATION and all accompanying pages.

ACE THE QUIZ

AGE	DIFFICULTY	PAGES
A & T	3	9

PURPOSE

To answer recovery related questions.

MATERIALS

Board, marker, 'ACE THE QUIZ' QUESTIONS, pages 164-166,
SCORESHEET, page 171,
ANSWER SHEETS, pages 167-170.
(Optional) prizes or play money (SKILLS BILLS pages 277, 278).

ATTENTION GRABBER

Draw and label vertical columns on board (select 5-6) and draw squares (6-8) in each –
draw a horizontal line midway to allow 3-4 boxes above and below in each column/category.
See Score Sheet, page 171.

Example: Love, Work, Sociology, Psychology, Physiology, Recovery, Spirituality, Panic, Fear,
Temptation and Family.

ACTIVITY

Divide into 2 teams. Label Team #1 above and Team #2 below horizontal line. 'Game Show
Host' alternates asking opposing teams questions. They select category and may collaborate with
teammates on answers. If one team cannot answer, opposite team gets the opportunity. Mark a
star on each box as each team answers. The first team to answer all 3-4 questions in each
category wins. See attached list of categories and questions.

FOLLOW-UP

Each tells the most important insight s/he developed today.

Note: Leader may copy entire score sheet onto board or select 5-6 categories due to time or
board space limitation. The score sheet could be taped onto board or clipboard if group
is small enough to be able to see it. They do need to visualize their boxes and/or stars as
the game progresses. Some prior knowledge is required for at least some participants
who can teach their peers. 'Game Show Host' and facilitator may accept any sensible
answer (those provided are suggested answers).

VARIATION

I. Facilitator may need to lead a brief discussion of each category first (using questions and
answers as a guide), if most participants are unfamiliar with the topics.

II. Although the provided questions address chemical dependency, any theme can be used.

III. Distribute questions 20 minutes before game. Allow teams to discuss and note answers in
advance.

Ace The Quiz

LOVE:
1. Why avoid entanglements the first year?
2. Why do drinks and drugs lead to fights?
3. If one lover quits alcohol or drugs and the other does not, what can happen?
4. When is separation necessary?
5. Why is having sex for the first time with someone a slippery situation?

WORK:
1. How is job performance affected by drinking and drugs?
2. What is the last thing to go? Why?
3. How can certain jobs lead to alcohol abuse?
4. How can some jobs lead to speed use?
5. How is job stress related to addiction?
6. How is unemployment related to addiction?
7. How can work help maintain sobriety?

SOCIOLOGY:
1. What is an environmental cue to drink or use?
2. How does peer pressure lead to alcohol or drug abuse?
3. How does peer pressure promote sobriety?
4. How does society glamorize drugs and alcohol?
5. What are slippery situations?
6. What people should we avoid?
7. What places should we avoid?
8. What is 'enabling'?

PSYCHOLOGY:
1. How does low self-esteem lead to addiction and addiction lead to low self-esteem?
2. How does guilt lead to addiction and addiction lead to guilt?
3. How does anger lead to addiction and addiction lead to anger?
4. How does negative thinking lead to addiction and addiction lead to negative thinking?
5. What is aversion therapy?
6. Are rewards or punishments more effective?
7. What negative effects do people suffer from when addicted?
8. What are the rewards of recovery?
9. Give examples of unhealthy relationships.
10. What makes relationships better in recovery?

ACE THE QUIZ

PHYSIOLOGY:

1. What happens to the central nervous system when you withdraw from alcohol?
2. What kind of prescribed drugs can be like alcohol in a pill for people with substance abuse problems?
3. What happens to the body and mind when you withdraw from speed?
4. What drug is most likely to cause extreme rage?
5. What organ detoxifies the body of alcohol and drugs?
6. Is addiction an acute or chronic disease?
7. Is it progressive? How?
8. Can alcoholism or addiction be inherited?
9. What chemical in our brain increases when we feel a 'rush'?
10. What happens to our ability to feel pleasure normally after using drugs or alcohol?
11. What is physical tolerance?
12. At first you drink or use to feel 'high', after a while, you drink or use to feel _____.
13. Is alcohol a stimulant or a depressant?
14. An overdose of alcohol can lead to _____.

RECOVERY:

1. What do they mean by 'recovery doesn't occur in a vacuum'?
2. What are some of the characteristics of a dysfunctional family?
3. What are the roles in a dysfunctional family?
4. What happens to the family when the addict gets clean?
5. What are the names of some 12-step programs?
6. Name two major components of AA, NA, or Dual Diagnosis Anonymous.
7. What are the benefits of meetings?
8. Why are sponsors so important?
9. What stops people from going to meetings?
10. Why do people delay getting a sponsor?
11. How can you help yourself?

SPIRITUALITY:

1. What is a Higher Power?
2. How have some religions made alcoholics and addicts feel?
3. How do you think your Higher Power views alcoholics and addicts?
4. What does 'turn it over' mean?
5. Name two benefits of going to a house of worship.
6. What do they mean by 'recovery is an inside job'?
7. What does this mean, "Our Creator doesn't make junk"?
8. How do you know your Higher Power is working in your life?
9. If your Higher Power could change one thing in your life, what would it be?
10. Recite the serenity prayer.

ACE THE QUIZ

PANIC AND FEAR
1. What can you do for hyperventilation?
2. If you are nervous, what chemical should you avoid?
3. What techniques help to calm us down?
4. What does it mean to identify the precipitating factor?
5. What is gradual desensitization?
6. Finish this quote –
   "The _____ of war is worse than war. We have nothing to fear but _____ itself."
7. What does the 'worst case scenario' mean? How does it help to think about it? Why shouldn't you dwell on it?
8. Explain "Do the thing you fear and the death of fear is certain."

TEMPTATION
1. Name three P's you should avoid.
2. What are 'déjà vu' dangers?
3. How can feeling a natural high help or hurt us?
4. How do depression and anxiety lead to temptation?
5. Name other dangerous emotions.
6. Explain HALT.

FAMILY
1. Who is an enabler?
2. Who is the hero?
3. Who is the scapegoat?
4. Who is the lost child?
5. Who is the class clown?
6. What sometimes happens to the family when the addict gets help?
7. What does a dysfunctional family teach us about reality? About feelings? If a person feels pain In a dysfunctional family what does s/he tend to do?
8. What happens when we ignore our negative feelings?
9. What are roles like in healthy families? Rigid or flexible?
10. Who needs treatment? Why?

ACE THE QUIZ

LOVE:

1. **Why avoid entanglements the first year?**
   The ups and downs of a relationship may lead to relapse
2. **Why do drinks and drugs lead to fights?**
   Thinking is distorted and self-control is decreased
3. **If one lover quits alcohol or drugs and the other does not, what can happen?**
   The sober one may relapse
4. **When is separation necessary?**
   Abuse, addiction, conflict that cannot be resolved
5. **Why is having sex for the first time with someone a slippery situation?**
   Nervousness or euphoria can lead to relapse

WORK:

1. **How is job performance affected by drinking and/or drugs?**
   Productivity, attendance, accidents, arguments
2. **What is the last thing to go?** *Job*
   Why? *Money for drugs and alcohol*
3. **How can certain jobs lead to alcohol abuse?** *Stress, entertaining customers or clients*
4. **How can some jobs lead to speed use?** *Unrealistic production pressure or very long hours*
5. **How is job stress related to addiction?** *Drink and/or use to relax*
6. **How is unemployment related to addiction?** *Depression, boredom, no schedule*
7. **How can work help maintain sobriety?** *Enhanced esteem, productive activity*

SOCIOLOGY:

1. **What is an environmental cue to drink or use?**
   Commercials, billboards, seeing people drink or use, drug paraphernalia
2. **How does peer pressure lead to alcohol or drug abuse?** *Want to 'fit in'*
3. **How does peer pressure promote sobriety?** *Meetings, sponsors*
4. **How does society glamorize drugs and alcohol?** *Movies, magazine ads, commercials*
5. **What are slippery situations?**
   People, places, things, emotions, physical conditions that can lead to relapse
6. **What people should we avoid?** *Drinkers, users, people who put us down*
7. **What places should we avoid?** *Any places we associate with drinking and/or drugs*
8. **What is 'enabling'?** *Helping people keep drinking and/or using by lying for them or providing money, food and/or shelter while they continue to drink and/or use*

Ace The Quiz

PSYCHOLOGY:

1. **How does low self-esteem lead to addiction and addiction lead to low self-esteem?**
   Use substance to feel good about ourselves; false confidence; do not develop social skills or talents and feel worse when substance wears off

2. **How does guilt lead to addiction and addiction lead to guilt?**
   Use substance to forget about undesirable behavior, then feel ashamed of drinking and/or using, or of behavior while under the influence

3. **How does anger lead to addiction and addiction lead to anger?**
   Use substance to suppress anger or to give ourselves an excuse to express it aggressively; angry when don't have the substance or angry at people who criticize substance abuse

4. **How does negative thinking lead to addiction and addiction lead to negative thinking?**
   Think sobriety can't be achieved and maintained so why try? Feel hung over or depressed due to crashing and think hopeless, helpless thoughts

5. **What is aversion therapy?** *Antabuse – a medicine that causes nausea, vomiting and other horrible symptoms if you drink.*

6. **Are rewards or punishments more effective?** *Rewards*

7. **What negative effects do people suffer from when addicted?**
   Legal, financial, relationship problems, mood swings, paranoia, health decline

8. **What are the rewards of recovery?**
   Esteem, serenity, physical and mental health, financial security

9. **Give examples of unhealthy relationships.**
   Unequal power, poor communication, no respect, one or both drinking and/or using

10. **What makes relationships better in recovery?** *Honesty, equality, respect*

PHYSIOLOGY:

1. **What happens to the central nervous system when you withdraw from alcohol?** *Overactive*

2. **What kind of prescribed drugs can be like alcohol in a pill for people with substance abuse problems?** *Tranquilizers, some sleeping pills and some pain killers*

3. **What happens to the body and mind when you withdraw from speed?** *Crash*

4. **What drug is most likely to cause extreme rage?** *PCP*

5. **What organ detoxifies the body of alcohol and drugs?** *Liver*

6. **Is addiction an acute or chronic disease?** *Chronic*

7. **Is it progressive?** *Yes*
   How? *Worsens over time*

8. **Can alcoholism or addiction be inherited?** *Yes*

9. **What chemical in our brain increases when we feel a 'rush'?** *Dopamine*

10. **What happens to our ability to feel pleasure normally after using drugs or alcohol?**
    At first, nothing compares to substance-induced pleasure; eventually, get a natural high from enjoyable activities

11. **What is physical tolerance?** *Need more to get same effect*

12. **At first you drink or use to feel 'high', after a while, you drink or use to feel _____.** *Normal*

13. **Is alcohol a stimulant or a depressant?** *Depressant*

14. **An overdose of alcohol can lead to _____.** *Death*

ACE THE QUIZ

RECOVERY:

1. **What do they mean by 'recovery doesn't occur in a vacuum'?**
   Need sponsor, meetings, step work

2. **What are some of the characteristics of a dysfunctional family?**
   Secrets, poor communication, unequal power, abuse, role changes

3. **What are the roles in a dysfunctional family?**
   Hero, Enabler, Scapegoat, Lost child, Mascot, Clown

4. **What happens to the family when the addict gets clean?**
   Roles change and some members dislike this

5. **What are the names of some 12-step programs?**
   Adult Children of Alcoholics, Alcoholics Anonymous, Narcotics Anonymous

6. **Name two major components of AA, NA, or Dual Diagnosis Anonymous.**
   Meetings and sponsor, step work

7. **What are the benefits of meetings?**
   Know you're not alone, get help from others who have been through similar problems, give help

8. **Why are sponsors so important?** *Individual support and guidance through the steps*

9. **What stops people from going to meetings?** *Fear, shyness, embarrassment*

10. **Why do people delay getting a sponsor?** *Fear rejection, not really ready to quit*

11. **How can you help yourself?**
    Go to meetings, get a sponsor, read recovery literature, and do the 12 steps

SPIRITUALITY:

1. **What is a Higher Power?**
   Something or someone larger than yourself; your inner voice; wisdom or truth

2. **How have some religions made alcoholics and addicts feel?** *Guilty, sinful*

3. **How do you think your Higher Power views alcoholics and addicts?** *With love and compassion*

4. **What does 'turn it over' mean?**
   Give the problem to your Higher Power after you've done all you can

5. **Name two benefits of going to a house of worship.** *Faith, new social support*

6. **What do they mean by 'recovery is an inside job'?**
   We must change our thoughts, feelings, and actions

7. **What does this mean, "Our Creator doesn't make junk"?**
   We are worthwhile versus worthless

8. **How do you know your Higher Power is working in your life?**
   You have strength to face challenges

9. **If your Higher Power could change one thing in your life, what would it be?**

10. **Recite the serenity prayer.** *Grant me the serenity to accept the things I cannot change, courage to change the things I can and the wisdom to know the difference.*

ACE THE QUIZ

PANIC AND FEAR

1. **What can you do for hyperventilation?**
   Blow into a paper bag or your hands, then breathe in the exhaled air
2. **If you are nervous, what chemical should you avoid?** *Caffeine*
3. **What techniques help to calm us down?** *Meditation, prayer, visualization, soothing music, deep breathing, progressive muscle relaxation, exercise*
4. **What does it mean to identify the precipitating factor?** *Find the person, place, thing, and substance that causes the panic* **Then what should we do?** *Avoid or learn to deal with it*
5. **What is gradual desensitization?** *Exposure to small parts of whatever we are afraid of*
6. **Finish this quote – " The _____ of war is worse than war. We have nothing to fear but _____ itself."** *Fear*
7. **What does the 'worst case scenario' mean?** *Picture the worst possible outcome*
   How does it help to think about it? *Decide how you would handle it*
   Why shouldn't you dwell on it? *Need to focus on positive outcomes*
8. **Explain "Do the thing you fear and the death of fear is certain."**
   If we're afraid of public speaking: talk at a meeting. If we're afraid of rejection: shake hands, ask someone to be our sponsor. If we're afraid of failure in school or work: take reasonable risks such as one class at a time or a job we qualify for and know that trying and doing our best is success regardless of other outcomes.

TEMPTATION

1. **Name three P's you should avoid.** *People, places, paraphernalia – things associated with substance such as wine glasses, pipes, straws used to snort, or syringes.*
2. **What are 'déjà vu' dangers?** *Sights, sounds, smells that trigger memories and cravings*
3. **How can feeling a natural high help or hurt us?** *Helps us learn we can improve mood without substances but hurts if we feel euphoric and invincible*
4. **How do depression and anxiety lead to temptation?** *Use substances for a quick but false 'fix'*
5. **Name other dangerous emotions.** *Anger, resentment, self pity, loneliness*
6. **Explain HALT.** *Don't get too hungry, angry, lonely or tired*

FAMILY

1. **What or who is an enabler?** *Person who 'covers' for addict or gives him/her money*
2. **Who is the hero?** *Usually oldest child – overachiever and caretaker*
3. **Who is the scapegoat?** *Takes the blame for family problems*
4. **Who is the lost child?** *Isolates and is often ignored*
5. **Who is the class clown?** *Uses humor to cover up true feelings or for attention*
6. **What sometimes happens to the family when the addict gets help?**
   At first _____? later _____? *Resentful, improved*
7. **What does a dysfunctional family teach us about reality?** *Don't think*
   About feelings? *Pleasant = good, painful = bad*   **If a person feels pain In a dysfunctional family what does s/he tend to do?** *Block it, ignore it, feel guilty*
8. **What happens when we ignore our negative feelings?** *They eventually worsen*
9. **What are roles like in healthy families? Rigid or flexible?** *Flexible*
10. **Who needs treatment?** *Alcoholic and whole family*
    Why? *Their roles and relationships change and the substance abuser needs support from others in recovery; family members need to learn about addiction, how to avoid enabling, and need support from other families facing similar challenges*

ACE THE QUIZ

SCORE SHEET

TEAM 1

TOPIC	TOPIC	TOPIC	TOPIC	TOPIC	TOPIC
☐ ☐ ☐	☐ ☐ ☐	☐ ☐ ☐	☐ ☐ ☐	☐ ☐ ☐	☐ ☐ ☐

TEAM 2

| ☐ ☐ ☐ | ☐ ☐ ☐ | ☐ ☐ ☐ | ☐ ☐ ☐ | ☐ ☐ ☐ | ☐ ☐ ☐ |

FACILITATOR'S INFORMATION
FORTUNE COOKIES

AGE	DIFFICULTY	PAGES
A & T	2	2

PURPOSE

To use excerpt from *Alcoholics Anonymous* as motivation for recovery and to link these rewards with the required work.

MATERIALS

Board, marker, container for CUT-UPS, tray of fortune cookies, *Alcoholics Anonymous* (commonly referred to as <u>The Big Book</u> - Alcoholics Anonymous World Services Inc., 3rd Edition), 'FORTUNE COOKIES' EXCERPT, page 173, cut into strips and folded, and intact copies of EXCERPT for FOLLOW-UP.

ATTENTION GRABBER

Display the cookies and discuss people's experiences with them.
Elicit the fact that 'fortunes' are NOT necessarily true.

ACTIVITY

Display *Alcoholics Anonymous* (<u>The Big Book</u>) and discuss its relevance to recovery. Place the excerpt (folded strips), on tray. Participants take turns selecting a sentence, writing it on the board, and discussing its relevance to their lives. Elicit the necessity of meetings, sponsors, step-work, <u>The Big Book</u> and recovery literature in reaping these rewards.

FOLLOW-UP

Distribute excerpt copies (following page). Each shares which sentences are most meaningful and why. Encourage them to develop additional personal goals and discuss how sobriety will help make them possible. Pass tray of fortune cookies and enjoy!

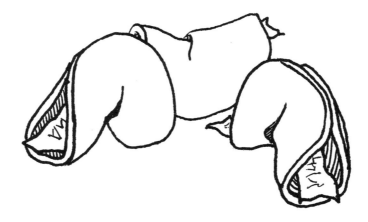

172

FORTUNE COOKIES

EXCERPT from pages 83-84 of ALCOHOLICS ANONYMOUS

If we are painstaking about this phase of our development, we will be amazed before we are halfway through. We are going to know a new freedom and a new happiness. We will not regret the past nor wish to shut the door on it. We will comprehend the word serenity and we will know peace. No matter how far down the scale we have gone, we will see how our experience can benefit others. That feeling of uselessness and self-pity will disappear. We will lose interest in selfish things and gain interest in our fellows. Self seeking will slip away. Our whole attitude and outlook upon life will change. Fear of people and of economic insecurity will leave us. We will intuitively know how to handle situations that used to baffle us. We will suddenly realize that God is doing for us what we could not do for ourselves.

Are these extravagant promises? We think not. They are being fulfilled among us — sometimes quickly, sometimes slowly. They will always materialize if we work for them.

NOTE: This excerpt from the book Alcoholics Anonymous, pages 83-84, is reprinted with permission of Alcoholics Anonymous World Services Inc., (A.A.W.S.) Permission to use this excerpt does not mean that A.A.W.S. has reviewed or approved the contents of this publication, or that A.A.W.S. necessarily agrees with the views expressed therein. A.A. is a program of recovery from alcoholism only — use of this material in connection with programs or activities which are patterned after A.A., but which address other problems or concerns, or in any other non-A.A. context, does not imply otherwise.

SAVE SANDY

AGE	DIFFICULTY	PAGES
A & T	1	2

PURPOSE

Apply slogans to own life.

MATERIALS

Board, marker, container for CUT-UPS, 'SAVE SANDY' CUT-UPS, page 175, and intact copies of CUT-UP page, one per participant.

ATTENTION GRABBER

Volunteer writes "SAVE SANDY" on board and draws a picture similar to the one below of "Sandy."

ACTIVITY

Distribute intact copies of CUT-UP page. Take turns reading slogans aloud. Then turn pages face down.
Take turns selecting a CUT-UP from container and putting slogan, one blank per letter, on board. As peers guess, insert letters.
List wrong letters on board. Take one body part away from Sandy for each wrong answer. Whoever guesses correct slogan takes the next turn.
If same person or people keep guessing correctly, they pick someone who has not had a turn to go next.
Whoever guesses the slogan must explain its relevance to his/her own life.

FOLLOW-UP

Each identifies his/her favorite slogan and gives the reason.

SAVE SANDY

1 Easy does it, but do it.	**2** Leave it there. Let it go.	**3** It works if you work it.
4 Live and let live.	**5** Turn it over, but you do the legwork.	**6** Think positive.
7 I can't. Someone can. I'll let him (steps 1-3)	**8** There is no problem so bad that a drink won't make worse.	**9** One drink is too many and a thousand aren't enough.
10 Switching from scotch to brandy.	**11** Keep it simple.	**12** One day at a time.
13 A drug is a drug.	**14** Pray for potatoes but keep on hoeing.	**15** First things first.
16 Trust your Higher Power.	**17** No slippery situations.	**18** HALT: Don't get too hungry, angry, lonely or tired.
19 Come, Come to, Come to believe.	**20** Living life on life's terms.	**21** To thine own self be true.

TIC-TAC-DOPE

AGE	DIFFICULTY	PAGES
A & T	3	6

PURPOSE

Answer recovery questions and develop insight.

MATERIALS

Board, marker, 'TIC-TAC-DOPE' QUESTIONS, pages 177, 178, ANSWER SHEETS, pages 179-181. (Optional) prizes or play money (SKILLS BILLS pages 277, 278).

ATTENTION GRABBER

Volunteer writes TIC-TAC-DOPE on board and draws  on board.

ACTIVITY

'Game Show Host' draws Tic-Tac-Toe game on board.
Two teams sit facing each other with 'Host' at board in front.
At bottom of board note players' names under 'X' or 'O' and keep score (number of games won by each team).
'Host' asks alternate teams the questions; a correct answer warrants an 'X' or 'O'; teammates should collaborate on answers and some questions require two or more people to respond.
If they answer incorrectly, the opposition tries.
Continue until one team wins or all spaces are filled.
If a tie occurs, the next question is the tie-breaker.
Whichever team answers correctly first, wins.
Erase board, appoint another 'Host' and continue until all questions have been answered.
Winners get first choice of prizes; the opponents select from the remaining prizes.
If no tangible rewards are available, discuss what everyone 'won' in terms of coping skills.

FOLLOW-UP

Each tells one new insight developed during the game.

VARIATION

Distribute QUESTIONS 20 minutes before game. Allow team to discuss and note answers in advance.

TIC-TAC-DOPE

1. Give an example of things to avoid.
2. How do drugs affect mental illness?
3. Give an example of continued use despite bad consequences.
4. How are energy and pleasure affected when we first stop drinking and/or using?
5. What is an example of alcohol in a pill?
6. What are some tools to reduce cravings?
7. What are some ways to naturally increase our dopamine?
8. Give an example of people to avoid.
9. What is compulsion?
10. What do drugs do?
11. Give an example of places to avoid?
12. What is denial?
13. What is dopamine?
14. What is tolerance?
15. What happens to dopamine when we use drugs?
16. What are late craving symptoms?
17. What is physical dependence?
18. How do drugs interact with prescribed medication?
19. What does HALT mean?
20. What is the problem when drugs cause very high levels of dopamine?
21. What is an environmental cue to use?
22. What are early craving signals?
23. What is an endogenous or inside cue to use?
24. Stress equals _____.
25. What are some natural drives?
26. What is easier than trying to figure out how many drinks you can safely have?
27. Why can't we drink or use just a small amount?
28. Which is worse – beer, wine or whiskey?
29. What is the 24-hour plan?
30. How does 'Live and Let Live' help us stay sober?
31. Can someone else 'drive us to drink?'
32. When you stop drinking and using, what do you need to do?

Tic-Tac-Dope

33. What can you do about your appearance and how does it help?

34. Give an example of something you cannot change. Each member of team must do this.

35. Give an example of something you can change. Each member of team must do this.

36. Give an example of an old routine you changed in order to stay clean and sober.

37. What type of food or drink usually stops an alcohol craving?

38. Each team: Raise your hand if you have a sponsor.

39. Why do people delay getting a sponsor?

40. Most recovering people are physically tired. Why?

41. Why is being tired or hungry to be avoided in recovery?

42. Why is addiction called 'The Lonely Disease?'

43. People use or drink to fit in, to be part of the crowd. How do we feel when it wears off?

44. What does AA or NA or DDA teach us that helps loneliness?

45. Why is it hard for 'loners' to join AA, NA or DDA?

46. What are loners 'green' at?

47. What is the reason many people get drunk?

48. What fears are often the causes of anger?

49. Tell a time you were angry because of fear of abandonment.

50. Tell a time you feared loss of control in a situation.

51. Tell a time you feared loss of 'face.'

52. What is TLC and why is it important in recovery?

53. Tell a way you can be good to yourself.

54. Why must we look out for over-elation or euphoria or celebrations?

55. Give an example of how 'easy does it' applies to your life.

56. Tell one thing you are grateful for.

57. Explain this: Remember your last drunk, not your first drink.

58. Tell a negative aspect of your last drunk or drug use.

59. Finish this sentence: A guy buys a new car and says, "With my luck it will be a _____."
    What kind of thinking is this?

60. What is the problem with self-pity?

61. What is a great weapon against self-pity?

62. Why are emotional entanglements crippling to recovery?

63. What is the 'If trap?'

64. Why is it foolish to tie sobriety to a person? Or to a circumstance?

TIC-TAC-DOPE

ANSWER SHEET page 1

1. **Give an example of things to avoid.**
   Anything associated with drinking and using – fancy wine glasses, straws, over-the-counter medicines for sleep or energy

2. **How do drugs affect mental illness?** *Worsen mood swings and paranoia*

3. **Give an example of continued use despite bad consequences.**
   Lose job or get DUI but keep drinking

4. **How are energy and pleasure affected when we first stop drinking and/or using?**
   Normal energy and/or pleasures are not experienced

5. **What is an example of alcohol in a pill?**
   Some tranquilizers, some sleeping pills or some pain killers

6. **What are some tools to reduce cravings?** *Exercise, talk, prayer, hot baths, writing, relaxation*

7. **What are some ways to naturally increase our dopamine?** *Exercise, safe sex, hobbies, sports*

8. **Give an example of people to avoid.** *Drinkers and/or users*

9. **What is compulsion?** *Loss of control – you must use and/or drink*

10. **What do drugs do?** *Give false pleasure*

11. **Give an example of places to avoid?**
    Parties, bars, or rock concerts – where alcohol and/or drugs are used

12. **What is denial?** *Temporary blindness to risks*

13. **What is dopamine?** *Chemical in brain – gives pleasure*

14. **What is tolerance?** *Need more and more to get high*

15. **What happens to dopamine when we use drugs?** *Increases*

16. **What are late craving symptoms?** *Urges – uncontrollable*

17. **What is physical dependence?** *Will get sick and/or have withdrawal symptoms without the substance*

18. **How do drugs interact with prescribed medication?**
    Intensify or counteract them and can be deadly

19. **What does HALT mean?** *Don't get too hungry, angry, lonely or tired*

20. **What is the problem when drugs cause very high levels of dopamine?**
    We don't feel natural pleasures

21. **What is an environmental cue to use?** *See the substance, related paraphernalia or people who are using the substance*

22. **What are early craving signals?** *Feel withdrawn, 'off', out of sorts*

23. **What is an endogenous or inside cue to use?** *Hunger, anger, depression*

24. **Stress equals _____.** *Craving*

25. **What are some natural drives?** *Food, water, sex*

179

TIC-TAC-DOPE

26. **What is easier than trying to figure out how many drinks you can safely have?**
    Stay away from the first drink

27. **Why can't we drink or use just a small amount?** *Triggers compulsion to take more*

28. **Which is worse – beer, wine or whiskey?** *All equally harmful and addictive*

29. **What is the 24-hour plan?**
    Schedule for one day at a time – meeting, step work, phone sponsor; plan for every hour

30. **How does 'Live and Let Live' help us stay sober?**
    We do not concern ourselves with what others think, say and/or do.

31. **Can someone else 'drive us to drink?'** *Only if we let them*

32. **When you stop drinking and using, what do you need to do?**
    Get active in Alcoholics Anonymous (AA), Narcotics Anonymous (NA) and/or Dual Diagnosis Anonymous (DDA) and in other areas of life – exercise, hobbies, school, volunteer, etc.

33. **What can you do about your appearance and how does it help?**
    Hair cut, get glasses, dental care, new clothes – all enhance self-esteem

34. **Give an example of something you cannot change. Each member of team must name something.** *Answers may include the past, other people, the weather, natural disasters*

35. **Give an example of something you can change. Each member of team must do this.**
    Answer may include attitudes, sobriety, self-care, employment, education

36. **Give an example of an old routine you changed in order to stay clean and sober. Each member answers.** *Example: not stopping at the bar after work.*

37. **What type of food or drink usually stops an alcohol craving?** *Sweet*

38. **Each team: Raise your hand if you have a sponsor.**
    The team with more hands raised gets the point.

39. **Why do people delay getting a sponsor?**
    Each person who does not have one tells why s/he is delaying.

40. **Most recovering people are physically tired. Why?** *They lost sleep or had poor nutrition when drinking and/or using.*

41. **Why is being tired or hungry to be avoided in recovery?** *Unmet physical needs trigger cravings.*

42. **Why is addiction called 'The Lonely Disease?'** *We can feel isolated even when around a lot of people and even if we're drinking and/or using together.*

43. **People use or drink to fit in, to be part of the crowd. How do we feel when it wears off?**
    Like more of an outcast

44. **What does AA or NA or DDA teach us that helps loneliness?**
    We are not alone and we are not so different.

45. **Why is it hard for 'loners' to join AA or DDA?** *Suspicious, defensive*

Tic-Tac-Dope

46. **What are loners 'green' at?** *Reaching out for friendship*

47. **What is the reason many people get drunk?** *"So I can tell somebody off."*

48. **What fears are often the causes of anger?** *Abandonment, loss of control, loss of face*

49. **Tell a time you were angry because of fear of abandonment.**

50. **Tell a time you feared loss of control in a situation.**

51. **Tell a time you feared loss of 'face.'**

52. **What is TLC and why is it important in recovery?**
    Give ourselves tender loving care to nurture and reward ourselves.

53. **Tell a way you can be good to yourself.**

54. **Why must we look out for over-elation or euphoria or celebrations?**
    We may think we are invincible and can safely drink or use.

55. **Give an example of how 'easy does it' applies to your life.**

56. **Tell one thing you are grateful for.**

57. **Explain this: Remember your last drunk, not your first drink.**
    Remember negatives, not the initial rosy glow.

58. **Tell a negative aspect of your last drunk or drug use.**

59. **Finish this sentence: A guy buys a new car and says, "With my luck it will be a _____."** *Lemon*
    What kind of thinking is this? *Negative or fortune telling.*

60. **What is the problem with self-pity?** *"Poor me, poor me, pour me a drink".*

61. **What is a great weapon against self-pity?** *Humor*

62. **Why are emotional entanglements often crippling to recovery?**
    The relationship takes priority; people forget meetings and stop calling sponsor.
    The ups and downs lead to relapse. A break-up or argument leads to relapse.

63. **What is the 'If trap?'** *"I'll stay clean if..."*

64. **Why is it foolish to tie sobriety to a person? Or to a circumstance?**
    We cannot control people or circumstances but we can control our attitudes and behavior regarding them.

FACILITATOR'S INFORMATION
WHAT'S A BAR?

AGE	DIFFICULTY	PAGES
A & T	2	2

PURPOSE

To identify the deficits of drinking and drug abuse; to identify and desire the rewards of recovery.

MATERIALS

Board, marker, pencils, broom or yardstick,
(anything to serve as a barrier; a chair or volunteer with outstretched arms will suffice),
'WHAT'S A BAR?' WORKSHEET, page 183.

ATTENTION GRABBER

Coach volunteer before group to stand at door and non-violently block peers from entering at start of group. After a few seconds, s/he allows entry.

Volunteer writes BAR on board. Ask, "What's a bar?" They'll probably answer, "A place where alcohol is served". Ask, "What was happening when you tried to come into the room today?" Elicit that they were 'barred' or blocked. Volunteer writes "BAR = to block or prevent entrance or success".

ACTIVITY

Distribute worksheet with 'The Bar' and related questions. Read poem in unison a few times. Discuss people's interpretations. Allow about fifteen minutes to write answers to worksheet questions. Discuss their responses.

FOLLOW-UP

Individuals, dyads or whole group composes relevant poems.
Topics may include, "What's A: Drink? Drug? Party? High? Hangover? Crash?"

VARIATION

I. People take turns selecting and writing two lines on board and applying them to their lives.

II. Facilitator or volunteers ask worksheet questions while participants answer orally.

III. Divide into dyads. Each questions partner, records responses, then 'presents' partner to the group and encourages feedback. "This is Tammy and her substance abuse barred her from…"

WHAT'S A BAR?

WORKSHEET

The Bar

The Saloon is sometimes called a Bar,
  A Bar to heaven, a door to hell
Whoever named it, named it well;
  A Bar to manliness and wealth
A door to want and broken health;
  A Bar to honor, pride and fame
A door to grief and sin and shame;
  A Bar to hope, a bar to prayer
A door to darkness and despair;
  A Bar to honored useful life
A door to brawling, senseless strife;
  A Bar to all that's true and brave
A door to every drunkard's grave;
  A Bar to joys that home imparts
A door to tears and aching hearts;
  A Bar to heaven, a door to hell
Whoever named it, named it well!

*By a convict serving
a life term in
Joliet Prison, Illinois*

1. How has your substance abuse barred you from 'heaven' or the good things in life? _____ _____

2. How has it led to 'hell' or misery? _____ _____

3. How has it interfered with your 'manliness' or 'womanliness'? _____ _____

4. Name at least two things you have lacked or had too little of due to substance abuse _____ _____

5. How has it (or will it) lead to 'broken' physical and mental health? _____ _____

6. How has it interfered with your honor, pride and/or fame? _____ _____

7. How has it led to your grief? _____
   sin?_____
   shame?_____

8. How has it destroyed your hope? _____

9. How has your substance abuse affected your spirituality? _____

10. How has it led to despair or depression? _____

11. How has it affected your productivity? _____

12. How has it led to arguments and affected your relationships? _____

13. How can it lead you to the grave? _____

14. How has it affected the joys of home and family? _____

15. When and how has it caused you to cry? _____

16. When and how has your substance abuse caused someone you care about to cry? _____ _____

17. How can you open the door to hope, health, honor, and happiness? _____ _____

18. What tools are helping you 'pry open' the 'bars' created by your substance abuse? (Discuss how you are *admitting* you have a problem, *asking* for help and *believing* you can do it.) _____ _____

19. Describe at least three components of your 'door' to recovery. (These may include details about step-work, meetings, therapy, medication if you also have emotional problems, working with a sponsor, spirituality, residential or out-patient recovery program, reading recovery literature and completing assignments, and others.)
_____
_____

RELATIONSHIPS

RELATIONSHIPS are difficult for people who have abandonment, enmeshment and/or abuse issues or whose delusions, distortions or hallucinations cause fear and distrust. They practice communicating and establishing healthy boundaries. People dealing with rebellion consider the power of kindness; people dealing with demoralizers learn self-protection.

ACTIVITY	PAGE NUMBERS	AGE	LEVEL OF DIFFICULTY	PAGES
Boomerangs	187	ALL	1	1
Circle Concepts	188	ALL	1	1
Everything You Always Wanted to ...	189 - 191	ALL, *A, *YP	1	3
Q and A	192	ALL	1	1
Terminators	193 - 195	ALL	2	3
Umbrellas	196 - 197	ALL	1	2
Win with Love	198 - 199	ALL	2	2

FACILITATOR'S INFORMATION
BOOMERANGS

AGE	DIFFICULTY	PAGES
ALL	1	1

PURPOSE

Recognize and practice 'kindness is returned with kindness'.

MATERIALS

Board, marker, pencils, crayon, paper.
(Optional) cardboard boomerang.

ATTENTION GRABBER

Volunteer displays boomerang or draws one on board and asks about its qualities.
(It comes back.)
Volunteer writes on board, "What goes around – comes around." Discuss.

ACTIVITY

Each shares a time s/he treated someone unkindly and received wrath.
Each tells a time s/he was kind and received kindness.

Ask, "When is it the most difficult to be kind." (When we are treated badly.)

Ask, "What are the benefits of being decent despite mistreatment?" (This does not apply to physical, sexual and verbal abuse but to petty annoyances, put downs and resentment.)

Each shares a current struggle with kindness or generosity, (example: mother-in-law visits and how it's hard to be friendly and share spouse's attention), identifies ways to be kind and anticipates results.

Ask, "What happens if we are decent and the person ignores it or reacts angrily despite our efforts?" (At least we know we behaved appropriately and did not 'stoop to that level'. Eventually the person may 'soften'.)

FOLLOW-UP

Discuss value of knowing we did the right thing and the 'boomerang' of self–esteem that results. Participants draw pictures of themselves, showing kindness in various situations, and/or role play the 'boomerang' effects of caring and generosity.

FACILITATOR'S INFORMATION
CIRCLE CONCEPTS

AGE	DIFFICULTY	PAGES
ALL	1	1

PURPOSE
Discuss healthy boundaries and identify if we are overshadowed by or smothering toward a significant other. Identify ways to achieve more closeness or distance.

MATERIALS
Board, marker, string, tape or chalk, pencils, papers.
(Be sure to retain the string or tape after group, as these could be dangerous.)

ATTENTION GRABBER
Volunteer makes a circle with string, tape or chalk and stands inside. Another 'invades his/her space' (circle) and asks, "How does it feel when I get in your personal space?" Discuss how it feels to be smothered by or obsessed with trying to control someone.

ACTIVITY
Draw circles on board and mark one, 'me'. Ask volunteers to guess which circle represents a stranger, an acquaintance, a close friend and a close family member, spouse or lover. (See attached diagram. Draw only the circles on board and have participants write the labels.)

Discuss the value (in the closest relationship) of some parts overlapping and some areas autonomous (the importance of shared interests and/or experiences and of maintaining individuality).

On board, someone depicts a person totally dominated by another (one circle on another with 95 - 100% overlap) and discusses what happens to each (consumed by the other) and the disadvantages of no individuality.

People draw circles on paper: themselves, and significant others in their lives and note how they feel about the relationships – they may wish they were closer or more independent. They should position their circles to portray their relationships and not copy exactly from the board. Possibly a parent and child or husband and wife may be far apart or enmeshed.

FOLLOW-UP
People share their drawings on board and receive peer feedback about their relationships. Brainstorm ways to achieve more closeness or distance. Discuss ways they have gained autonomy from a domineering person or given 'space' to someone they tried to control. Emphasize balance of unity and individuality in healthy relationships.

NOTE: The goal is not to do in depth relationship therapy but to identify healthy versus unhealthy boundaries and to refer for professional therapy as needed. Physical or sexual abuse may be discovered and warrants individual discussion, reporting and referral.

Example:

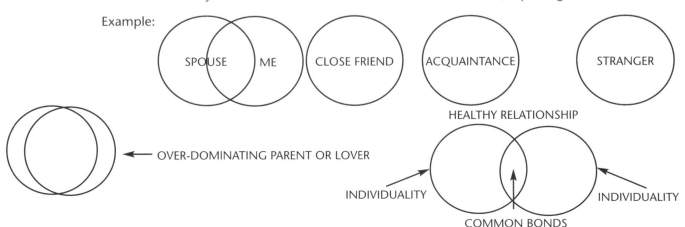

OVER-DOMINATING PARENT OR LOVER

FACILITATOR'S INFORMATION
Everything You Always Wanted to Know...
But Were Afraid To Ask!

AGE	DIFFICULTY	PAGES
ALL *A *YP	1	3

PURPOSE To communicate openly versus seeking negative attention.

MATERIALS 'EVERYTHING YOU ALWAYS WANTED TO KNOW...' QUESTIONS for ADULTS, page 190, and QUESTIONS for YOUNG PEOPLE, page 191.

ATTENTION GRABBER Ask, "Have you ever felt the opposite sex was a mystery?" Explain: "You will have the chance to find out everything you have ever wanted to know but were afraid to ask."

ACTIVITY Males and females sit at opposite sides of room or table facing each other. Take turns asking and answering questions. Example: First female asks the panel of males, question one, then first male asks female panel a question.

FOLLOW-UP Participants share at least one new thing they learned about the opposite sex.

VARIATION Have each sex develop their own 10-20 questions to ask the opposite sex panel. Set ground rules regarding off-limit topics such as money, looks or sexual prowess. The facilitator must decide in advance what is appropriate and inappropriate concerning looks and sexuality. It may be beneficial to address promiscuity in terms of disliked behavior or evidence of low self-esteem or to include chastity or fidelity as a preferred quality. Appearance may be addressed (neat and clean) but beauty, handsome-ness, body-build, etc., should be downplayed.

NOTE: People who are bisexual, gay or lesbian may substitute 'mate' or 'partner' for 'man' or 'woman' on QUESTIONS pages.

EVERYTHING YOU ALWAYS WANTED TO KNOW... BUT WERE AFRAID TO ASK!

QUESTIONS for ADULTS

MEN ASK WOMEN:

Describe 3 qualities that attract you to a man.

Describe 3 'turn-offs'.

Do you prefer a man who has or has not been married before and why?

Are you willing to become involved with a man who has custody of his children? Why or why not?

How does a partner's drinking or drug use affect your relationship?

Describe ways you'd like your partner to handle conflict and/or anger.

How does a partner's mental illness affect a relationship? Discuss the value of medication and therapy.

Discuss honesty in a relationship. What should both people disclose? What, if anything, should be kept private?

How important is your family's approval of your mate? Under what circumstances would you date or marry a man your parents or kids disliked?

Would you become involved with a man whose family you disliked? Why or why not?

- -

WOMEN ASK MEN:

Describe 3 qualities that attract you to a woman.

Describe 3 'turn-offs'.

Do you prefer a woman who has or has not been married before and why?

Are you willing to become involved with a woman who has custody of her children? Why or why not?

How does a partner's drinking or drug use affect your relationship?

Describe ways you'd like your partner to handle conflict and/or anger.

How does a partner's mental illness affect a relationship? Discuss the value of medication and therapy.

Discuss honesty in a relationship. What should both people disclose? What, if anything, should be kept private?

How important is your family's approval of your mate? Under what circumstances would you date or marry a woman your parents or kids disliked?

Would you become involved with a woman whose family you disliked? Why or why not?

Everything You Always Wanted to Know...
But Were Afraid To Ask!

QUESTIONS for YOUNG PEOPLE

GUYS ASK GIRLS:

What 3 qualities do you look for in a guy?

How can guys show you respect? (3 ways at least)

If a guy gets mad, how do you want him to act? (at least 3 'do's' and 3 'don'ts')

If a guy is sad or his feelings are hurt, what do you want him to do?

Give 3 examples of 'show off' or phony behavior you have seen in guys.

Name at least 3 behaviors you dislike in guys.

Tell the nicest thing you ever saw a guy do.

Tell the worst thing you ever saw a guy do.

Tell at least 3 ways a guy shows he has low self–esteem.

Tell at least 3 ways a guy shows he has high self–esteem.

GIRLS ASK GUYS:

What 3 qualities do you look for in a girl?

How can girls show you respect? (3 ways at least)

If a girl gets mad, how do you want her to act? (at least 3 'do's' and 3 'don'ts')

If a girl is sad or her feelings are hurt, what do you want her to do?

Give 3 examples of 'show off' or phony behavior you have seen in girls.

Name at least 3 behaviors you dislike in girls.

Tell the nicest thing you ever saw a girl do.

Tell the worst thing you ever saw a girl do.

Tell at least 3 ways a girl shows she has low self-esteem.

Tell at least 3 ways a girl shows she has high self–esteem.

FACILITATOR'S INFORMATION
Q AND A

AGE	DIFFICULTY	PAGES
ALL	1	1

PURPOSE

Practice asking open-ended questions and reflecting feelings.

MATERIALS

Board, marker, chairs arranged in a circle.

ATTENTION GRABBER

What do people often worry about in social situations? Elicit – "What do we talk about?"

ACTIVITY

Explain: "We are going to practice two communication techniques to use with friends and/or family to help in conflict resolution." Select volunteer to ask peer a question that can be answered with yes or no or with one word. Select another to ask a question to really get someone talking. Differentiate between closed and open questions and list some 'open' questions on board. "How do you feel about...", "Tell me about...", "What is your opinion about...", etc.

Each asks an open-ended question of the person on his/her left. Then those who answered questions ask one of the person on their right.

Next, select a volunteer to share an emotional experience and a peer to reflect his/her feelings (restate in different words). Practice asking person on left, "Tell me about a time you felt mad, sad, happy, afraid, etc." The listener paraphrases with emphasis on feelings.

Next, reverse roles. People on the left, who just shared an emotional experience, ask peers to their right to share about a time they felt mad, sad, etc., and summarize their responses.

FOLLOW-UP

Discuss benefits of open-ended questions and reflecting feelings (get people talking, show understanding and/or empathy) and how this might help if two people have a difference of opinion. Each states a time in the near future s/he can use these skills (on a date, at dinner table, with parent, child, spouse, etc.). Encourage elaboration on with whom, what issue, when, where, how they'll approach the subject. Encourage role-playing the anticipated interactions.

TERMINATORS

AGE	DIFFICULTY	PAGES
ALL	2	3

PURPOSE

Identify blocks to communication and practice communication enhancers or 'openers'.

MATERIALS

Board, marker, 'TERMINATORS' with EXAMPLES, page 194,
with DEFINITIONS AND PROBLEMS, page 195.
(Optional) prizes or play money (SKILLS BILLS, pages 277, 278).

ATTENTION GRABBER

Place row of chairs touching each other a few feet from board (to create an obstacle). Ask volunteer to write on board. As the person tries, ask, "What's the problem?" Elicit that s/he cannot get to the board and discuss problems with blocks or barriers. Volunteer then writes 'Terminators' on the board (after the chair blockade has been removed).

ACTIVITY

Discuss 'TERMINATORS' that shut down communication. Encourage participants to brainstorm blocks to conversations. Then have volunteers take turns introducing the terms on the list of 'TERMINATORS' with DEFINITIONS AND PROBLEMS, page 195. The participants who write on the board see the definition and elicit related information from peers. Example: S/he copies a term and asks peers – "What do you think this means? What's the problem?"

After discussing definitions and problems, 'Game Show Host' lists terms (but not examples) in RANDOM ORDER from the provided list of terminators with examples. Divide into 2 teams with chairs facing each other and 'Host' at front near board, reading one example at a time. First team tries to guess the matching term. If correct, they accrue a point or play money. If incorrect, the other team guesses. 'Game Show Host' alternatively gives each team the opportunity to guess the 'Terminator' for each example. Team with most points or play money wins.

FOLLOW-UP

Brainstorm ways to enhance communication. List, discuss and then role-play these 'openers'.
Eye contact.
Face the person.
Open posture, arms at side or in lap but not crossed or folded.
Participants insert their own topics below.
"How do you feel about . . . "
"What is your opinion about . . . "
"Tell me about . . . "
"What is your impression of . . . "

TERMINATORS

TERMINATORS with EXAMPLES

Instructions: 'Game Show Host' lists the 'Terminators' terms on board in RANDOM ORDER. S/he then reads an example (in quotations) and takes turns giving teams the opportunity to guess the correct term. 'Host' must be sure terms on board are in a <u>different</u> order than shown below!

<u>TERMS:</u>	<u>EXAMPLES:</u>
REFUTING:	"You don't either" "What makes you think so?" "You're a liar."
INTERPRETING:	Someone says; "My dog is a mutt" and you say "You're ashamed of your dog."
JUDGING:	"What a good person you are." "You're disgusting."
ADVISING:	"If I were you. . ." "Here's what you should do. . ."
INTERRUPTING:	"Excuse me, but . . ." Blab, blab, blab
CHANGING THE SUBJECT:	"What's for dinner tonight?" "What's the weather going to be tomorrow?"
PROBING:	"Where did you get your coat?" "How much did it cost?"
OVERUSE OF HUMOR:	"This is a great joke about death."
DOMINATING:	"Whatever you say or do, I can top it."
PUTTING DOWN:	"That's stupid." "You jerk!"

Terminators

REFUTING: arguing, trying to disprove a statement; insisting a belief or opinion is untrue.

Problem: causes anger; you're refusing to hear an opposing point of view.

INTERPRETING: trying to explain someone's statement based on your own beliefs.

Problem: putting your own 'spin' on something prevents seeing it from another perspective.

JUDGING: deciding that people, statements and/or beliefs are good or bad based on your own values.

Problem: you're not respecting different values; if you degrade people, they shut down. Labeling someone or something 'good' means you may later label someone or something 'bad'.

ADVISING: recommending how you would handle a situation.

Problem: people view their problems as unique and rarely want advice. They prefer to share thoughts and/or feelings; let them 'bounce' ideas off you!

INTERRUPTING: talking when someone else talks.

Problem: people will shut down or talk over you; when two people talk, no one is listening.

CHANGING THE SUBJECT: talking about an unrelated topic (usually due to disagreement or discomfort).

Problem: gives the message that someone's issue is unimportant or taboo.

PROBING: asking very personal questions; digging for information in a pushy way.

Problem: people feel their privacy is invaded and they 'clam up'.

OVERUSE OF HUMOR: laughing or joking about serious topics.

Problem: people feel their problems are insignificant; you show your own discomfort with certain subjects.

DOMINATING: trying to prove you have a bigger and/or better accomplishment or a worse problem.

Problem: makes the person and his / her issues seem unimportant.

PUTTING DOWN: making nasty comments; name-calling.

Problem: people fear talking if it results in insults.

PURPOSE

To achieve an internal locus of control; to maintain hope, joy and esteem despite people's attempts to destroy these.

MATERIALS

Board, marker, container for CUT-UPS, umbrella or drawing of umbrella on board, 'UMBRELLAS' CUT-UPS, page197.

ATTENTION GRABBER

Volunteer displays umbrella or draws one on board. Ask, "When do we need an umbrella?" Elicit that it protects us.

Volunteer writes on board, "People can rain on your parade only if you let them."

(From *Shoot For The Moon* by Meiji Stewart, copyright 1996 by Meiji Stewart. Reprinted by permission of Hazelden Foundation, Center City, MN.)

ACTIVITY

Ask participants to interpret the quote. Elicit that people can ruin our mood only if we let them. Encourage sharing about people who tried to destroy their hope, joy and esteem.

Ask, "What motivates people to try to destroy our hope, joy and esteem?" Encourage them to "consider the source": Hurtful people may feel inferior, envious, unhappy, angry at someone or something else, or may have been told or taught these negative thoughts.

Explain, "Our thoughts and actions serve as our umbrellas. When it is your turn, state at least one thought and one action to protect yourself from someone's *'rain'*."

People take turns selecting and copying a CUT-UP example on board, then stating protective thoughts and actions. (Answers should incorporate assertive, positive statements and goal-oriented actions.)

Examples: "You'll never amount to anything." Participant might say, "I believe I will", and sign up for High School Equivalency or vocational training classes; or "I am already a worthwhile person", and seek out people who believe in him/her. "You always screw up." Participant might say, "I am learning from my mistakes", and keep trying .

FOLLOW-UP

Each shares a time s/he did not let someone *'rain'* on his/her *'parade'*. (If someone has always given power to the negative comments, ask how s/he could have protected herself/himself.)

Ask , "Is it possible to *'rain'* on your own *'parade'*?" Discuss importance of monitoring and changing our own negative self-talk. Discuss importance of avoiding *'raining'* on other peoples' *'parades'*.

VARIATION

Participants anonymously write the disheartening comments or actions on pieces of paper. These are substituted for CUT-UPS, or used as supplements.

Umbrellas

1 "Don't get your hopes up."	**2** "You'll never amount to anything."	**3** "You're just like your _____ (father, mother, sister, brother)."
4 "You're always screwing up."	**5** "You act like a dummy."	**6** "You're just spinning your wheels."
7 "If something can go wrong, it will."	**8** "You're fat" or "You're ugly."	**9** "You're nobody special."
10 "Your idea will never work."	**11** "People just use you."	**12** "Nobody likes you."
13 "You'll never be promoted" or "You'll never graduate."	**14** "You're a lousy _____ (parent, son, daughter, student, worker, husband, wife, lover)."	**15** "It will never happen."
16 "You're just a day dreamer."	**17** "You're in for a rude awakening."	**18** "I don't want to burst your bubble, but......."
19 "It won't last."	**20** "You'll never get married, have a partner, or be loved."	**21** "You're sunk."
22 "You'll never change."	**23** "You're useless."	**24** "You'll never measure up."

197

FACILITATOR'S INFORMATION
WIN WITH LOVE

AGE	DIFFICULTY	PAGES
ALL	2	2

PURPOSE

To repair a hostile relationship with compassion, empathy and love.
To prevent resentful retaliation.

MATERIALS

Board, marker, chalk, string or tape, 'WIN WITH LOVE' WORKSHEET, page 199.

ATTENTION GRABBER

Before group, coach one volunteer to play 'rebel', who eventually 'softens', and another to portray the 'peacemaker'. Place chair inside circle drawn on floor with chalk, string or tape. Be sure to retrieve string or tape after group.

'Rebel', with angry facial expression and clenched fists, sits inside circle. Brainstorm and list on board ways people draw 'circles' or 'walls' around themselves to shut others out. Examples may include anger outbursts, isolation and superiority.

Ask "How do we feel when someone acts rebellious?" Discuss times participants acted angry and resentful toward a 'rebel'.

'Peacemaker' enters circle, smiles and extends hand. 'Rebel' smiles and shakes hands.
Ask, "What changed the 'rebel's' behavior?" (Compassion and recognition that the person was probably hurting emotionally).

ACTIVITY

Distribute worksheet with "Outwitted" by Edwin Markham and related questions. Introduce possibly unfamiliar terms: HERETIC – person with opinions opposed to official or established rules; FLOUT – to mock, scorn or show contempt. Read poem in unison a few times and discuss people's interpretations. Allow about fifteen minutes for participants to write answers to worksheet questions. Discuss their responses.

FOLLOW-UP

Participants role play current conflicts and practice approaching their 'rebel' with love. *Emphasize these principles do not promote submissive responses to physical, emotional or sexual abuse!*

VARIATION

I. Facilitator or volunteers ask worksheet questions while participants answer orally.

II. Divide into dyads. Each asks partner the questions, records responses, then 'presents' partner to the group and encourages feedback. " This is Randy. Someone shut him out when…"

WIN WITH LOVE

WORKSHEET

Outwitted

He drew a circle that shut me out-
Heretic, rebel, a thing to flout.
But Love and I had the wit to win:
We drew a circle that took him in!

by Edwin Markham

---

* "Outwitted" is reprinted by permission of Horrmann Library, Wagner College, Staten Island, New York.

1. When and how did someone you care about shut you out with anger, rebelliousness or other behavior?
   _____

2. When and how did you show contempt or 'coolness' toward that person? _____
   _____

3. How did your contempt or 'coolness' affect the relationship? _____
   _____

4. When and how did you show kindness toward that person? _____
   _____

5. How did your kindness affect the relationship? _____
   _____

6. Explain the last two lines of the poem in your own words. _____
   _____

7. Tell about two times you 'won over' an angry person with love or kindness. _____
   _____

8. With whom are you currently having conflicts? _____
   _____

9. How can you show love, understanding or compassion? _____
   _____

10. How might the person's behavior change? _____
    _____

11. Whether or not the person changes, how do <u>you</u> benefit from showing kindness? _____
    _____

12. When were you the 'rebel' and how were you helped by someone's love or compassion? _____
    _____

SELF-DEVELOPMENT requires awareness of defenses, needs, values, beliefs, positive visualization and goal-directed actions. Participants clarify these through pictorial, verbal and written representations.

ACTIVITY	PAGE NUMBERS	AGE	LEVEL OF DIFFICULTY	PAGES
Basic Needs per Maslow	203 - 205	A & T	2	3
Defense Mechanisms	206 - 208	A & T	2	3
KISS	209 - 210	A & T	2	2
Masks	211	ALL	1	1
Realistic Goal Setting - Accept Half a Loaf	212	ALL	1	1
Stages	213 - 215	A & T	2	3
Talk Show Host	216	ALL	1	1
The Mind's Eye	217	ALL	1	1
This is Your Life	218 - 219	A & T	1	2
To Tell the Truth	220 - 222	A & T	2	3

LEGEND

AGES:
ALL = ALL ages, 8 or 9 through adults
YP = YOUNG PEOPLE, ages 8 or 9 through 17
T = TEENS, ages 13 through 17
A & T = ADULTS and TEENS, ages 13 and older
A = ADULTS, ages 18 and older
* = SPECIFIC PAGES expressly for this population.

LEVEL OF DIFFICULTY:
1 = EASIER - basic language; minimal reading and writing
2 = MODERATE - introduces new terminology; incorporates life experiences
3 = MORE DIFFICULT - requires some prior knowledge or introduction of new information; promotes peer teaching

PAGES:
The total number of pages related to the activity, including FACILITATOR'S INFORMATION and all accompanying pages.

BASIC NEEDS PER MASLOW

AGE	DIFFICULTY	PAGES
A & T	2	3

PURPOSE

Identify positive ways to meet each need as defined by Abraham Maslow.

MATERIALS

Board, marker, 5 slips of paper with one need on each, large drawing paper, pencils, crayons. If allowed, instant camera and photo of each participant and scotch tape.
'MASLOW'S HIERARCHY OF NEEDS' QUIZ, page 204.

ATTENTION GRABBER

Volunteer draws triangle on board divided into 5 sections.
Ask – "What do we need in order to live?" Elicit: Air, food and water.
Participant writes "Physiological" on board (they use slip for correct spelling) in bottom section of triangle.
Ask – "If our physical needs are met, what do we need?"
Ask questions about each need, moving up the hierarchy. Add key words to board as they brainstorm requirements for each need. (Examples: food, air, water; houses, doors, locks; family and friends; passing grades, good grooming; reaching a personal or career goal)
Discuss threats to each need such as: Being abused, drugs and/or alcohol, seeking love and belonging through gangs. Discuss positive ways to meet each need. Review concepts of this theory using 'MASLOW'S HIERARCHY OF NEEDS' FACILITATOR'S GUIDE, page 205.

ACTIVITY

Each goes to board, places photo (or initials) next to the need s/he is currently trying to meet. Each explains how s/he satisfied lower needs positively. Group suggests ways to move up the hierarchy. Distribute QUIZ, page 204. Individuals, dyads or teams decide upon answers (more than one may apply for each). They share and discuss answers as a group.

FOLLOW-UP

Debate this question: "Must you fulfill each lower need before moving to a higher one?" (Many people believe you must but accept any logical answers as the purpose is to promote thought and discussion, not to prove any response right or wrong.)

VARIATION

Each draws triangle, labels sections and depicts him/herself meeting each need in a positive manner.

ANSWER KEY for QUIZ, page 204.
NOTE: the major need being satisfied or threatened is listed but any plausible answer may be accepted.

1. B, C	2. E, D
3. C	4. A, B (C & D are affected also)
5. A, B (C & D are affected also)	6. A, D
7. D	8. A, B (C & D are affected also)
9. D	10. A, D
11. E, D	12. E, D
13. C, B	14. A, B, C, D
15. D	16. C, D

MASLOW'S HIERARCHY OF NEEDS

QUIZ

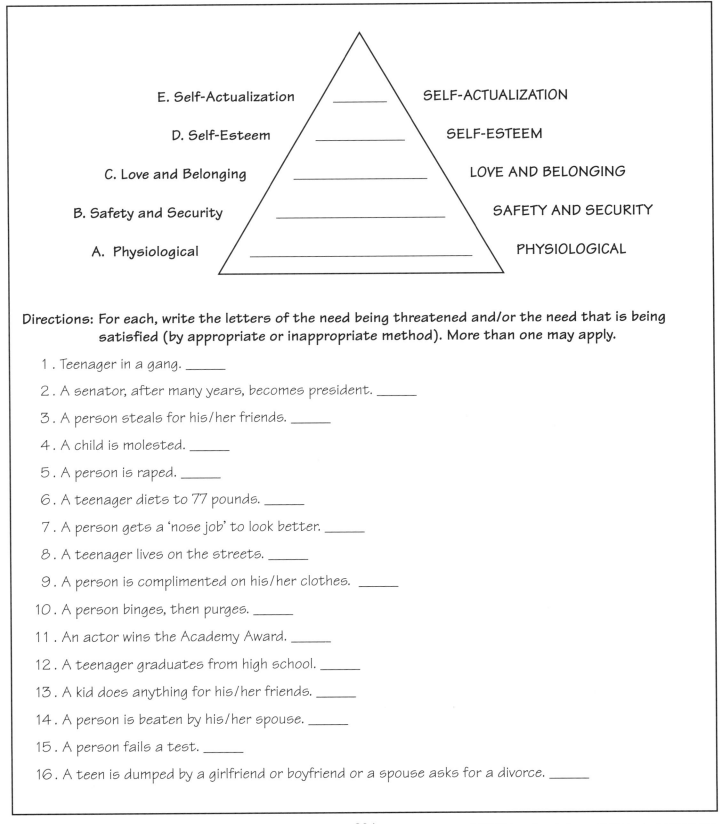

E. Self-Actualization _____ SELF-ACTUALIZATION

D. Self-Esteem _____ SELF-ESTEEM

C. Love and Belonging _____ LOVE AND BELONGING

B. Safety and Security _____ SAFETY AND SECURITY

A. Physiological _____ PHYSIOLOGICAL

Directions: For each, write the letters of the need being threatened and/or the need that is being satisfied (by appropriate or inappropriate method). More than one may apply.

1. Teenager in a gang. _____

2. A senator, after many years, becomes president. _____

3. A person steals for his/her friends. _____

4. A child is molested. _____

5. A person is raped. _____

6. A teenager diets to 77 pounds. _____

7. A person gets a 'nose job' to look better. _____

8. A teenager lives on the streets. _____

9. A person is complimented on his/her clothes. _____

10. A person binges, then purges. _____

11. An actor wins the Academy Award. _____

12. A teenager graduates from high school. _____

13. A kid does anything for his/her friends. _____

14. A person is beaten by his/her spouse. _____

15. A person fails a test. _____

16. A teen is dumped by a girlfriend or boyfriend or a spouse asks for a divorce. _____

MASLOW'S HIERARCHY OF NEEDS

Abraham Maslow emphasized fulfillment of biological and psychological needs and developed a hierarchy presuming the more basic physiological needs must be satisfied before moving upward. They are usually depicted as a triangle with the most basic at bottom.

PHYSIOLOGICAL: (at base of triangle) – air, water, food, medical care

SAFETY AND SECURITY: shelter, clothing, locks, laws, and rules

LOVE AND BELONGING: hopefully met by family and friends; met also by spouse or partner, affiliating with others in clubs, organizations, churches, temples, schools, neighborhood, community activities

SELF-ESTEEM: accomplishments at school and work, hobbies, volunteering, positive feedback, good grooming, productive activity (occupational therapy, art, drama, music, writing, and crafts)

SELF-ACTUALIZATION: reaching full potential including accepting self and/or others, self care while recognizing the needs and desires of others, unique responses (versus mechanical, stereotyped), spontaneity, creativity, assertiveness. May encompass personal and/or career achievements.

NOTE: When brainstorming, do not 'split hairs' over examples which may fit into two categories.
  Example: clothing might fit into Physiological (prevent freezing to death) or Safety and Security or Esteem.
  Reaching a career goal might encompass Esteem and Self-Actualization.
  Threats to meeting the needs may overlap.
  Example: homelessness impacts Physiological, Safety and Security, Love and Belonging, Esteem and Actualization.
  Physical or sexual abuse encompasses many.
  'Looking for love in all the wrong places' is exemplified by promiscuity and/or joining gangs which thwarts genuine Love and Belonging as well as Safety and Physiology.
  Identifying their needs and differentiating between healthy and unhealthy ways to meet them is the goal.

To learn more about Maslow:

Pervin, L.A. and O.P. Jordan, Personality Theory and Research 7th ed., John Wiley and Sons, New York, 1997.

Lester, D. and J. Hvezda, S. Sullivan and R. Pluorde, "Maslow's Hierarchy of Needs and Psychological Health," Journal of General Psychology, Vol. 109, pp. 83-85.

FACILITATOR'S INFORMATION
DEFENSE MECHANISMS

AGE	DIFFICULTY	PAGES
A & T	2	3

PURPOSE

To identify defense mechanisms and their use and/or misuse.

MATERIALS

Board, marker, 'DEFENSE MECHANISMS' MATCHING QUIZ, page 207,
FACILITATOR'S GUIDE, page 208.
(Optional) prizes or play money (SKILLS BILLS pages 277, 278).

ATTENTION GRABBER

Volunteer lies on floor in fetal position. Ask, "What's represented?" (S/he looks like a baby.)
Introduce 'regression' and ask when and why it's used. Volunteer writes 14 terms (only) on
board.

A. Denial
B. Regression
C. Rationalization
D. Compromise

E. Sublimation
F. Substitution
G. Transference
H. Repression

I . Compensation
J . Intellectualization
K . Fantasy

L . Conversion Reaction
M. Displacement
N. Blaming

ACTIVITY

Review terms as needed, using FACILITATOR'S GUIDE, page 208. Divide into two teams.
'Game Show Host' reads examples using 'DEFENSE MECHANISM' MATCHING QUIZ, page 207
items #1-18. Teams take turns guessing the answers from the 14 terms on board. They accrue
points or play money for correct responses. Team with the most points wins.

FOLLOW-UP

Personalize: Each shares which defense mechanisms s/he frequently uses or misuses. Discuss
ways to break down defenses and that they sometimes serve a useful purpose but are usually
misused or over-used.

VARIATION

The MATCHING QUIZ, page 207, can be used for the team questions and/or for an individual or
small group project.

ANSWER KEY for 'DEFENSE MECHANISM' MATCHING QUIZ, page 207.

1. A	2. J	3. B	4. C	5. D	6. E
7. I	8. K	9. L	10. M	11. G	12. H
13. I	14. A	15. N	16. L	17. F	18. F

DEFENSE MECHANISMS

MATCHING QUIZ

A . Denial
B . Regression
C . Rationalization
D . Compromise

E . Sublimation
F . Substitution
G . Transference
H . Repression

I . Compensation
J . Intellectualization
K . Fantasy

L . Conversion Reaction
M . Displacement
N . Blaming

_____ 1 . "I'm not an addict or alcoholic. I'm just a social user."

_____ 2 . "There is a theory about oral fixation which applies to me."

_____ 3 . Four-year old drinks from a baby bottle.

_____ 4 . "I drink because my mother left me at age 4."

_____ 5 . "I'll meet you half way."

_____ 6 . Sexual energy channeled into sports.

_____ 7 . "I'm too short for basketball so I'll be a runner."

_____ 8 . "I'm a famous rock star."

_____ 9 . A soldier's shooting hand is paralyzed.

_____ 10 . A mad kid kicks the cat.

_____ 11 . "That therapist reminds me of my dad."

_____ 12 . "I don't remember my childhood abuse."

_____ 13 . "I'm not athletic but I'm great in math."

_____ 14 . "I'm not depressed. I'm not suicidal."

_____ 15 . "It's my parent's fault that I'm messed up."

_____ 16 . A new father becomes deaf because he doesn't want to hear his baby cry.

_____ 17 . "I quit drugs a year ago. I'm clean. I just drink a 12-pack on Saturdays."

_____ 18 . "When I feel like carving on my arm, I write in my journal or draw."

DEFENSE MECHANISMS

Defense mechanisms serve a protective purpose to decrease anxiety, but are often over-used and maladaptive.

1. **DENIAL** - Ignore or refute an unpleasant fact or situation. Helps us through the initial trauma, but then we must recognize and cope with truth. ("My husband is not dead." is acceptable during the early stage of grief. Setting a place for him at the table weeks later is not healthy.) Denial of mental illness or substance abuse delays or prevents treatments.

2. **REGRESSION** - Go back to an earlier, safer, more comfortable stage, situation or behavior. (Fetal position, thumb sucking in an older, frightened child).

3. **RATIONALIZATION** - making excuses for inappropriate behavior. ("I just drink to unwind.")

4. **SUBLIMATION** - (often positive) finding a healthy outlet for a potentially unacceptable impulse- an angry person chops wood or sexual energy is diverted into sports.

5. **TRANSFERENCE** - a person reminds you of someone you liked or disliked and you infer they have similar characteristics and treat them accordingly. (Participants rebel against group leaders who remind them of authority figures.)

6. **REPRESSION** - you 'press down', stuff, bury unpleasant events. (People sometimes 'forget' abuse.)

7. **INTELLECTUALIZATION** - avoidance of emotion; being in your head verses your heart, similar to rationalization.

8. **CONVERSION REACTION** - a physical problem related to a psychological one. (Someone sees a murder and becomes temporarily blind.)

9. **DISPLACEMENT** - taking anger or other emotions out on someone else. (Your boss gives you constructive criticism and you go home and berate your spouse.)

10. **FANTASY** - using the imagination. Can be a lifesaver: a prisoner of war daydreams about return to family. Can be dangerous: a stalker thinking someone is in love with him/her. Can prevent facing reality: parents are getting divorced and child pretends they will be together forever.

11. **SUBSTITUTION** - can be negative (switching from beer to prescription tranquilizers). Can be positive (draw or cut up paper or talk instead of carving on wrist.)

12. **COMPENSATION** - making up for deficits: Can be positive: your report writing is mediocre but you are great with people. You volunteer to handle daily crises while a colleague does extra paperwork. Can be negative: you feel inferior and compensate by doing double the work of everyone else.

13. **COMPROMISE** - (a positive mechanism) meeting someone halfway. This is a conflict resolution skill, but considered a defense mechanism by some resources.

14. **BLAMING** – stating that someone or something causes your unhealthy behavior.

To learn more about Defense Mechanisms, consult:
Rollant, Paulette D. and Denise B. Deppoliti, <u>Mental Health Nursing</u>, Mosby's Review Series, Mosby Yearbook, Inc., St. Louis, MO., 1996.

FACILITATOR'S INFORMATION
KISS

PURPOSE

Express thoughts and clarify own values.

MATERIALS

Board, marker, candy kisses, container for CUT-UPS, 'KISS' CUT-UPS, page 210.
Names of participants in a cup or bowl, if variation is used.

ATTENTION GRABBER

Show a candy kiss and ask, "What's it called?" Volunteer writes 'KISS' on the board.
Ask what the letters stand for.
Discuss 'Keep It Simple Smartie' (versus 'Keep It Simple Stupid').

ACTIVITY

Each participant takes a turn in the 'spotlight seat' and reads and answers a question.
Emphasize: Each is entitled to his/her opinion. There are no right or wrong answers.
As each leaves the 'spotlight seat', s/he gets a candy kiss as a reward.
To 'Keep it Simple' remind people to answer the question with specifics, stick to the topic, and impose a time limit for each response (3 minutes or whatever is appropriate).

FOLLOW-UP

Each shares one new insight developed during group.

VARIATION

Sit in circle or at a table. Each writes his/her name on a scrap of paper. Place these in a cup or bowl. People take turns drawing a name. They then read a question and ask that person (whose name was drawn) to answer.

QUESTIONS

1 With whom do I compare myself to and how does it affect me?	**2** What does it mean to be a caretaker?	**3** Explain: Practice makes perfect.
4 Tell about a healthy relationship in my life.	**5** Tell how I overcame a fear of failure.	**6** How has fear of abandonment affected me?
7 What is defeat? (answer must involve concept that defeat is the first step to something better)	**8** What is the difference between constructive and destructive criticism?	**9** Explain: "There is nothing either good or bad but thinking makes it so." *from HAMLET by William Shakespeare*
10 How do I stop being a victim?	**11** Can we control our thoughts and feelings? Tell 3 ways to control each.	**12** A time I manipulated someone and how I could have been honest and received what I wanted:
13 What does being moral mean to me?	**14** A time I _____ (drank, used, overate, cut on myself) because of anger and what I could have done instead was:	**15** Describe 3 of my strengths and 3 weaknesses. How can I better utilize my assets and improve my limitations?
16 Are people without formal education dumb? Why or why not?	**17** What is a 'self-fulfilling prophecy'? Tell a time I measured up to my expectations. Tell a time I expected, then experienced failure.	**18** Does money buy happiness? Why or why not?

FACILITATOR'S INFORMATION

AGE	DIFFICULTY	PAGES
ALL	1	1

PURPOSE

To identify and express hidden feelings and/or traits.

MATERIALS

Mask, pencils, crayons, paper.

ATTENTION GRABBER

Volunteer walks in wearing mask.
Ask, "Why do we wear masks?"
Elicit that we may portray a tough or cheerful image because we fear people's reactions to our true emotions.

ACTIVITY

Group members draw the facial expressions and images or representations they show the world, on one side of the paper. On the other side, they depict innermost feelings and traits. Encourage use of symbols, words and phrases to portray concepts, if they cannot depict everything. They share their drawings and hear how others see them.

Examples of drawings:
　　Smiling to the world; crying on the inside.
　　Tough and mean on the outside (angry facial expression, big muscles, clenched fist);
　　　　sad and fearful on the inside.
　　Neutral facial expression on outside; gritting teeth or biting tongue on the inside.

FOLLOW-UP

Discuss the importance of being genuine and the appropriate time, place and person for disclosures.

Realistic Goal Setting
Accept Half a Loaf

AGE	DIFFICULTY	PAGES
ALL	1	1

PURPOSE

To accept a partial gain, to set 'mini' goals and reach compromises.

MATERIALS

Board, marker, loaf of bread. (Optional) paper and pencils.

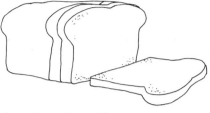

ATTENTION GRABBER

Volunteer removes approximately 8 pieces of bread. Ask, "What do we have?"
Elicit: "Half a loaf." Ask, "What does it mean to accept half a loaf?"
Elicit concepts: We can't always have everything our own way.
Sometimes we need to be satisfied with partial goal attainment or compromises.

ACTIVITY

Each writes and tells a time s/he got part of what s/he wanted.
(Example: popcorn and a video at home instead of dinner out and a movie.)

Each tells a time s/he accepted a step toward a goal. (Example: Wanted to graduate from college but achieved a High School diploma or wanted an 'A' average but improved D - F grades to B - C grades.)

Each tells a time s/he reached a 50/50 compromise with a friend, or significant other.
(Example: Wanted a curfew of midnight and parents wanted 10 p.m. They settled for 11 p.m.)

People share a current situation wherein they want something intensely and identify how they can accept 'half a loaf.' Discuss stepping stones toward a long term goal or a compromise about an important issue (versus a superficial example).

Encourage group members to assist each other or work in dyads. If in pairs, they ask the question, "Tell about a current situation. How can you accept, 'half a loaf', use stepping stones and/or reach a compromise?" Write partner's response, then present partner to the group – "This is Jane and her situation is … "

FOLLOW-UP

Debate this question: "Are there times we should not settle for 'half a loaf'?"
Describe the exceptions. (Examples include accepting NO physical abuse or putting 100% effort toward an important goal.)

FACILITATOR'S INFORMATION
STAGES

AGE	DIFFICULTY	PAGES
A & T	2	3

PURPOSE

To describe Erikson's developmental tasks or stages and own progress throughout the continuum.

MATERIALS

Board, marker, 'STAGES' CUT-UPS, page 214, and FACILITATOR'S GUIDE, page 215.

ATTENTION GRABBER

Volunteer draws only continuum on board (with no labels) under title 'Stages.'
Elicit concepts about chronological development –
    we learn to crawl, walk, run, read, write, drive, work, and other activities
    at different ages and stages.

ACTIVITY

Take turns writing the task from 'STAGES' CUT-UPS, page 214, on continuum and eliciting peer interpretations. (No need to note ages, just correct sequence). Review stages using FACILITATOR'S GUIDE, page 215.

Each goes to the board and describes how s/he struggled with and completed each stage and how s/he will meet the challenges of upcoming stages.

1	2	3	4	5	6	7	8
Trust versus Mistrust	Autonomy versus Doubt	Initiative versus Guilt	Industry versus Inferiority	Identity versus Role Confusion	Intimacy versus Isolation	Generativity versus Self Absorption	Ego Integrity versus Despair

Note: Goal is to realize how participants mastered or can master each. (Even if they are not middle-aged or older, they can still discuss generativity versus self-absorption and ego integrity versus despair.)

FOLLOW-UP

Each tells his/her easiest and most difficult task and why.

VARIATION

Each goes up to board and discusses Trust vs. Mistrust. Then each goes up and discusses Autonomy versus Doubt, and so forth until all have been addressed. They must give specific examples of how they developed trust, autonomy, initiative, etc.

STAGES

1 TRUST VERSUS MISTRUST	**2** AUTONOMY VERSUS DOUBT
3 INITIATIVE VERSUS GUILT	**4** INDUSTRY VERSUS INFERIORITY
5 IDENTITY VERSUS ROLE CONFUSION	**6** INTIMACY VERSUS ISOLATION
7 GENERATIVITY VERSUS SELF ABSORPTION	**8** EGO INTEGRITY VERSUS DESPAIR

TRUST VERSUS MISTRUST: usually accomplished during infancy, with a close caregiver and leads to hope, feeling good about self and others, optimism. If early needs are not met, person may develop sense of badness, mistrust and pessimism.

AUTONOMY VS. DOUBT AND SHAME: usually accomplished in early childhood, ages two to three, with parent figures, and leads to exercise of own will, control, making choices. If unmet, person may be overly rigid, self-conscious with dominating sense of conscience and/or shame.

INITIATIVE VS. GUILT: usually accomplished during pre-school years, ages four to five, with family, and leads to sense of purpose and direction. If unmet, person may feel guilty about working toward aspirations.

INDUSTRY VS. INFERIORITY: usually accomplished during elementary school or pre-teens, with classmates, teachers and neighborhood associates, and leads to productivity and pride in accomplishments. If unmet, person may feel incompetent or inadequate to complete tasks.

IDENTITY VS. ROLE CONFUSION: usually accomplished during adolescence, with peers and leadership models, and leads to stable self-concept and career planning. If unmet, the person may feel uncomfortable in roles, phony, and lack individualism.

INTIMACY VS. ISOLATION: usually accomplished in young adulthood, with partners and friends, and leads to genuine love and sharing. If unmet, the person may be superficial and avoid intimacy.

GENERATIVITY VS. STAGNATION AND/OR SELF-ABSORPTION: usually met in adulthood, with family, coworkers and/or community, and leads to satisfying relationships and productive activity. If unmet, the person may lose interest in relationships and activities and may focus too much on self.

INTEGRITY VS. DESPAIR: usually met in the senior years, through satisfaction with self, significant others and accomplishments, and leads to contentment and pride in wisdom developed throughout life. If unmet, the person may feel bitter, fearful, and hopeless.

To learn more about Erikson's theory of psychosocial stages of development, consult:
Pervin, L.A. and O.P. Jordan, <u>Personality Theory and Research</u> 7th ed., John Wiley and Sons, New York, 1997.

Talk Show Host

AGE	DIFFICULTY	PAGES
ALL	1	1

PURPOSE ▶ To explore self, problems, progress, coping skills.

MATERIALS ▶ Board, marker, pencil, paper.
List of questions on relevant topics.
Use examples below or develop others.
Chairs arranged with 2 in front, facing 'audience' and the rest in a semi-circle or in rows.

ATTENTION GRABBER ▶ Ask, "What are talk shows?" and discuss people's favorites.

ACTIVITY ▶ Take turns playing 'host' and 'guest' and sitting in front, facing 'audience', who participates by asking questions and giving suggestions.

NOTE: Topics and questions can be decided upon by facilitator before group or developed by all participants (brainstorm and list them on board) or they can work in dyads or small teams to develop topics and questions.

FOLLOW-UP ▶ Each tells one new fact s/he learned about him/herself and one peer during the group.

Examples:
What led you to come to this program? What changes have you recently made?
Tell us about one decision with a negative outcome. Now share a decision that was beneficial to you.
Tell us about one significant person in your past and how s/he influenced you. Who exerts negative influence on you now? Who provides positive influence on you and why?
Discuss how a hobby, sport, pet or job helped you emotionally in the past. What now provides similar satisfaction? (If nothing, 'audience' and 'guest' can brainstorm possibilities.)
Tell us when and/or why you started drinking, what made you decide to stop, how you got help, how you are maintaining sobriety (including step-work, meetings, working with a sponsor) and your relapse prevention plan.
Share with us a time one door closed and another one opened. What did you do to create or capitalize on the opportunity?
Tell us one thing in your life you must accept because it cannot be changed and something you can change. How do you plan to make the change? What have you done to improve the situation?
Tell us how you overcame an obstacle in the past. Share about how you are overcoming a current problem.

FACILITATOR'S INFORMATION
THE MIND'S EYE

AGE	DIFFICULTY	PAGES
ALL	1	1

PURPOSE

Visualize positive steps toward goals.

MATERIALS

Board, marker, toy brain with toy eye inside, paper, crayons, pencils.

ATTENTION GRABBER

Pass around a plastic brain with 'eye' (See NOTE below)
Participants shake it and guess what's inside. Volunteer opens the brain and shows the eye.
Ask, "What would be another way of saying 'a brain with an eye'?"
Elicit concepts: 'The mind's eye' and 'What we see is what we get.' Discuss the dangers of
    negative and benefits of positive visualization.
Example: "If you're about to run a race and you see yourself falling flat on your face, what could
    happen?
What should you picture?" (See yourself running your best.)
Focus on positive behavior, not the outcome.

ACTIVITY

Participants draw, in collage manner, everything helpful they'll do during the next 6 months.
They may include school, work, health-related activities, taking psychotropic medicine and going
to therapy, going to support groups and/or place of worship. Share drawings and if pertinent,
on other side, draw themselves reaching long-term goals (graduation, getting a home, family or
whatever they desire).

FOLLOW-UP

Participants share their drawings and receive feedback. Then, with eyes closed, they practice
visualizing and describing their positive behavior related to current goals and/or challenges.

VARIATION

For the 12 steps of Alcoholics Anonymous, Narcotic Anonymous, Dual Diagnosis Anonymous or
other 12-step programs: Group members draw themselves doing each step or each draws one
step. Combine them for a bulletin board.

NOTE: A model brain and eye may be purchased separately through school instructional
materials catalogs or in toy sections of stores. Often the 'eyes' are gumballs or on
keychains. If there are none available, they can easily be made. An empty plastic egg
(sold with panty hose or putty) can represent a brain. A marble or gumball can represent
an eye. Be inventive (and humorous)!

FACILITATOR'S INFORMATION
THIS IS YOUR LIFE

AGE	DIFFICULTY	PAGES
A & T	1	2

PURPOSE

Maximize growth in all areas.

MATERIALS

Board, marker, paper, pencils, crayons, glue or tape,
'THIS IS YOUR LIFE' WORKSHEET, page 219.

ATTENTION GRABBER

Volunteer draws circle with 8 pie-shaped divisions on board.
Tell group, "This is your life," and ask them what's important to their quality of life.

ACTIVITY

Participants take turns writing key words on board (family, social, physical, spiritual, vocational, emotional, intellectual, financial). Discuss how we can reach our maximum potential in each area. People copy the circle and labels, then draw themselves doing things necessary for their growth in each area. They share their drawings and receive feedback.

FOLLOW-UP

Each ranks the 8 categories in order of their importance to him/her and identifies whether s/he places too much or too little value on any category. Discuss ways to achieve better balance.

VARIATION

On their paper, ask participants to divide circle into the 8 categories BUT size of sections must show amount of attention and effort they put into each. Instruct them to cut labels and tape or glue in desired section. When they share their drawings, at a glance they and their peers see if one or two areas are over-emphasized and which ones are being ignored. Discuss ways to achieve better balance.

Examples:

A 'workaholic' who is obsessed with money

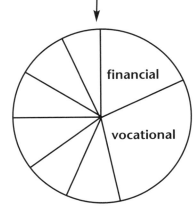

A person who puts friends ahead of family or work, school, etc., or a physical fitness buff who goes to extremes.

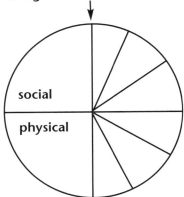

THIS IS YOUR LIFE

WORKSHEET

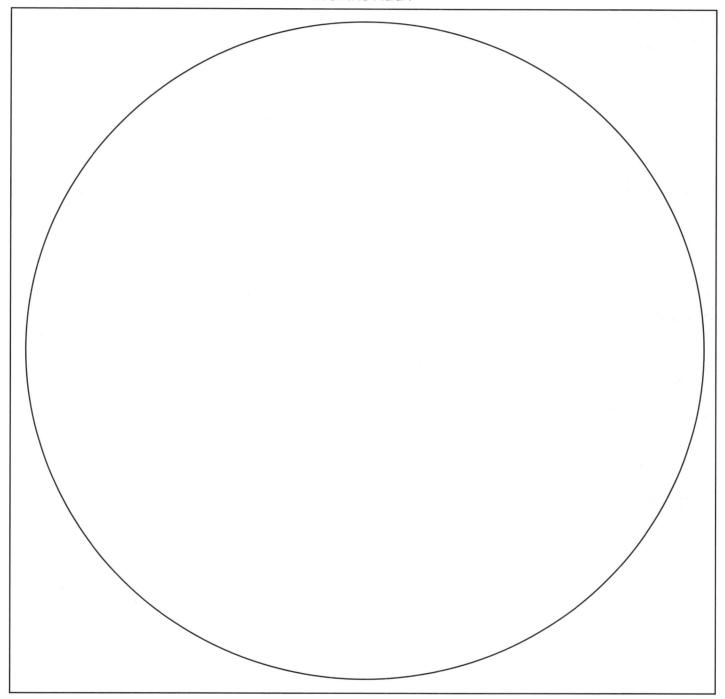

FAMILY	VOCATIONAL	SOCIAL	EMOTIONAL
PHYSICAL	INTELLECTUAL	SPIRITUAL	FINANCIAL

219

AGE	DIFFICULTY	PAGES
A & T	2	3

PURPOSE

Identify and express thoughts, values, issues and solutions.

MATERIALS

Board, marker, 'TO TELL THE TRUTH' QUESTIONS, pages 221, 222.
(Optional) prizes or play money (SKILLS BILLS pages 277, 278).

ATTENTION GRABBER

Volunteer writes on board 'To Tell the Truth.'
Explain: "We are playing a game. You choose a category from this list and answer the question."
　　　List categories on board:
　　　　　FEELING IMPORTANT
　　　　　SELF-FULFILLING PROPHECY
　　　　　LOVE AND BELONGING
　　　　　SELF-AWARENESS
　　　　　MISCELLANEOUS

ACTIVITY

Appoint person to keep score or dole out play money (SKILLS BILLS). Divide into 2 teams. 'Game Show Host' asks question of first person in first team. If s/he answers, his/her team gets the point or play money. If s/he declines, first person in opposing team gets opportunity. The questions have no right or wrong answers so no one would lose points due to limited knowledge or poor academic skills. The point would be lost if they refuse to try. Almost any answer is acceptable that does not glamorize drugs, alcohol, gangs, violence and/or death. Truthful answers get points or play money. The consequence for no answer is other team can answer and accrue points or play money. See attached list of questions for each category.

FOLLOW-UP

Discuss two things each learned about him/her self.

TO TELL THE TRUTH

A. FEELING IMPORTANT

1. What happens when we compare ourselves to others? Tell a time you did and how you felt.
2. Name a job some people think is low status and tell why it is very important.
   Does our job title (or lack of employment) define our worth? Why not?
3. On a scale of 100%, how much importance do you place on your looks?
   Would you like to place less or more importance on appearance and why?
4. Tell a time you acted superior to cover feelings of inferiority. Why is this ineffective?
5. Under what circumstances should your own needs come first?
   When should you put someone else's needs first?
6. A challenge you face now is:
7. On a scale of 100%, how much importance do you place on educational achievement?
   Would you like to place more or less importance on it and why?
8. Do your actions speak louder than words? How?
9. What do you think, say, do that makes you feel insignificant?
   What do you think, say, do that makes you feel important?
10. How much importance do you place on your material possessions and/or finances
    (on 100% scale)? Do you want to place more or less importance on this and why?

B. SELF-FULFILLING PROPHECY

1. How does the way we treat others and our expectations of them affect their behavior?
   Tell a time you expected the worst and got it.
   Tell a time a person measured up to positive expectations.
2. What can you tell yourself to help you see the good in someone who is behaving badly?
3. How do your expectations influence your behavior?
   Tell a time you expected the worst and best from yourself and the results.
4. Explain positive reinforcement and how it affects another's and your own behavior. Tell times you
   rewarded someone else and yourself for appropriate behavior. Describe some intangible rewards.
5. Why is ignoring bad behavior often the most effective consequence?

C. LOVE AND BELONGING

1. What is the problem with trying to measure up to someone else's standards?
   Tell a time you failed at this. Name five standards you have set for yourself.
2. When we feel rejected, what are three negative and three positive ways to respond?
3. Tell about a relationship where love and belonging depended on your accomplishments.
   What is the problem?
4. Why is self-love a prerequisite to being loved by others?
   Name five ways you demonstrate self-love.
5. How does the way we feel about ourselves determine how others treat us? Tell a time you had
   low esteem and were treated badly. Tell a time you were treated well because of high esteem.
6. When a friendship or love relationship ends, how do you feel? Tell a time you thought it was the
   end of the world but survived. Tell a time a relationship ended but you found a better one.
7. Is it better to be alone or with the wrong person and why?
   What can you do to prevent feeling lonely when not in a relationship?
8. Why is self-development easier when you're not in an intense relationship?
   How can you ensure someone you love does not engulf you?

To Tell The Truth

D. SELF-AWARENESS

1. When something good happens to someone, what is your first response?
   What do you do about it?
2. On a scale of 100% - how much control do you have over your past, present and future?
   Do you need to increase or decrease these percents and why?
3. Five limitations and five assets of yours are: _____ _____ _____ _____ _____
   _____ _____ _____ _____ _____
4. A fork in the road you now face is _____ (or one you faced recently). Discuss.
5. What three things motivate you?
6. What are your 'sore spots' or what 'pushes your buttons'? (Name at least two)
7. What does happiness mean to you?
   Name two things you can think about and two things you can do to be happy.
8. Tell about one mistake and what you learned from it.
9. Tell about at least two aspects of your life:
   Choose from – social, intellectual, physical, spiritual, financial, vocational.

E. MISCELLANEOUS

1. When you make a mistake, do you usually admit it, avoid the subject or cover it up? Tell a time
   you blamed someone or something else. What happens when we deny, avoid, or blame?
   Tell a time you accepted responsibility for an error.
2. Do we learn more from winning or losing? Tell a time you learned from defeat.
3. If money didn't matter, what would you like to do for a job? What would you get out of it?
4. What makes you nervous? (name the top 3).
   Discuss 'Just do it' or 'Do the thing you fear and the death of that fear is certain.'
5. Discuss concept of 'worst case scenario.' Tell about a risk you need to take –
   what is the worst case scenario and how will you handle it? What's the best case scenario?
   What is the most likely outcome?

SELF-ESTEEM

SELF-ESTEEM is imperative because feelings of guilt, failure and worthlessness often underlie depression, self-harm, aggression and suicidal ideation. Personal, social and vocational growth is stunted. Participants practice acting confident, doing productive activities including helping others, giving and receiving positive feedback, thereby enhancing self-esteem.

ACTIVITY	PAGE NUMBERS	AGE	LEVEL OF DIFFICULTY	PAGES
Act As If	225	A & T	1	1
Go Getters	226 - 227	A & T	1	2
Success	228 - 229	A & T	2	2
Volunteer	230	A & T	2	1
What's In A Name?	231	ALL	2	1

LEGEND

AGES:
ALL = ALL ages, 8 or 9 through adults
YP = YOUNG PEOPLE, ages 8 or 9 through 17
T = TEENS, ages 13 through 17
A & T = ADULTS and TEENS, ages 13 and older
A = ADULTS, ages 18 and older
* = SPECIFIC PAGES expressly for this population.

LEVEL OF DIFFICULTY:
1 = EASIER - basic language; minimal reading and writing
2 = MODERATE - introduces new terminology; incorporates life experiences
3 = MORE DIFFICULT - requires some prior knowledge or introduction of new information; promotes peer teaching

PAGES:
The total number of pages related to the activity, including FACILITATOR'S INFORMATION and all accompanying pages.

FACILITATOR'S INFORMATION
ACT AS IF

AGE	DIFFICULTY	PAGES
A & T	1	1

PURPOSE

Practice acting *confident* despite fears; *kind* despite resentment; *controlled* despite agitation, etc.

MATERIALS

Board, marker.

ATTENTION GRABBER

Volunteer writes "Act As If..." on board.
Elicit that it's effective to act as if we feel calm and confident in a difficult situation.

ACTIVITY

Brainstorm and have a 'recorder' list on board situations that are embarrassing, stressful and annoying. (Examples: First date; fall flat on your face at a job interview; someone calls you a name; you are asked a question you can't answer in class; you spill something on your boss; you have to give a speech; you attend a party with strangers; your ex-lover's current girlfriend/boyfriend tells you how much they are loved; you have to talk with a person who got the promotion you sought; etc.)

Role-play acting calm, confident, kind, etc. in these situations (each person picks the most relevant one).

FOLLOW-UP

Discuss concept of 'act your way into good thinking' and have each tell a time s/he did this.

Ask,

"Does 'acting as if' mean we should **always** hide our true feelings?" (no)

"When **should** we 'let it all hang out'?" (with counselor, significant other, doctor, therapist)

"How does this differ from wearing a 'mask' or being phony?" ('Masks' and phoniness **hide** our true feelings; 'acting as if' allows us to **practice** appropriate **behavior** despite our feelings. We may **change** our feelings as a result of 'acting as if'.)

GO GETTERS

AGE	DIFFICULTY	PAGES
A & T	1	2

PURPOSE

Practice confident, goal-oriented actions.

MATERIALS

Board, marker, phone book, newspaper and telephone, container for CUT-UPS, 'GO GETTERS' SITUATIONS CUT-UPS, page 227.
(Optional) Community College, Adult Education, YMCA, YWCA brochures.

ATTENTION GRABBER

Volunteer writes 'GO GETTERS' on board and asks what it means.
Explain, "We're going to act like confident Go-Getters."

ACTIVITY

Take turns reading a situation aloud and role-playing actions.
They must:
1. Talk about thoughts and plans
2. Go through the motions

Example: "You want to further your education" – the person might verbalize "I can do it – I'll start with one class and work up to a full schedule." S/he will then look through classified ads or phone book, make mock phone call about registration and request information or a catalog.

FOLLOW-UP

Each shares a time s/he was fearful or reluctant but took positive action and achieved results.

VARIATION

Group members write current troublesome or challenging situations on slips of paper and these are randomly drawn or each person describes his/her own situation and receives peer suggestions as needed.

Go Getters

SITUATIONS

1 You want to further your education.	**2** You want someone to go on a trip with you.
3 You have a health problem.	**4** You want a volunteer job.
5 Someone breaks up with you.	**6** You have a problem in a relationship.
7 You want a pet.	**8** You have an emotional problem.
9 You want to stop a bad habit.	**10** People put you down.
11 You want to move to a different place.	**12** You want to join a church, temple or house of worship.
13 You want a roommate.	**14** You need new clothes.
15 You want to learn a new skill.	**16** You want companionship.
17 You want new furniture.	**18** You want to go out with someone on a date.
19 You would like to be friends with someone.	**20** You want a raise in pay or a promotion.
21 You are with strangers at a new school, job or neighborhood.	**22** You want more time to yourself.

Success

AGE	DIFFICULTY	PAGES
A & T	2	2

PURPOSE

To define success in terms of behavior and traits.
To de-emphasize external measures (money, power, status, title, material possessions).
To strive for achievable goals.

MATERIALS

Board, marker, 'SUCCESS' WORKSHEET, page 229.

ATTENTION GRABBER

Volunteer writes 'SUCCESS' on board, and lists responses as peers brainstorm what constitutes success.

ACTIVITY

Distribute 'SUCCESS WORKSHEET', page 229, with "Success" by unknown author and related questions. Read poem in unison a few times, and discuss people's interpretations. Allow about fifteen minutes for participants to write answers to worksheet questions. Discuss their responses.

FOLLOW-UP

Volunteer prints SUCCESS vertically on board and records peer suggestions for related words or phrases. Example:

     S - self-acceptance
     U - understanding
     C - cheerful despite disappointment
     C - challenging yourself
     E - enthusiasm
     S - spirituality
     S - seeing the good in self and others

Each shares how his/her perception of success changed during the activity and identifies his/her most significant component of success.

VARIATION

I. Facilitator or volunteers ask worksheet questions while participants answer orally.

II. Divide into dyads. Each asks partner the questions, records responses, then 'presents' partner to group and encourages feedback. "This is Debbie. Some ways she used to define success are..."

SUCCESS

Success

Success is speaking words of praise,
In cheering other people's ways,
In doing just the best you can,
With every task and every plan,
It's silence when your speech would hurt,
Politeness when your neighbor's curt,
It's deafness when the scandal flows,
And sympathy with others' woes,
It's loyalty when duty calls,
It's courage when disaster falls,

It's patience when the hours are long,
It's found in laughter and in song,
It's in the silent time of prayer,
In happiness and in despair,
In all of life and nothing less,
We find the thing we call success.

Author Unknown

1. When and how did you define your success in terms of money, possessions, power, status, title, or other role or accomplishment?
   _____
   _____

2. What is the problem with external measures of success?
   _____
   _____

3. When and how did you praise or cheer-up someone?
   _____
   _____

4. When and how did you do your best on a task or plan regardless of the outcome?
   _____
   _____

5. When were you silent when your speech would hurt?
   _____
   _____

6. When and how were you polite despite someone's rudeness?
   _____
   _____

7. When and how did you refuse to respond to gossip? _____
_____

8. When and how did you show sympathy? _____

9. When and how were you loyal when duty called? _____
_____

10. When and how did you show courage despite disaster? _____
_____

11. When and how did you show patience? _____

12. Tell about the most recent time you laughed. _____

13. Tell about the most recent time you sang. _____

14. Tell about a recent experience with silent prayer, meditation, inspiration or affirmation. _____
_____

15. What were you doing the most recent time you felt happiness? _____
_____

16. The author states success is also found in despair. What success have you experienced in seemingly hopeless circumstances? Do **not** focus on the events or outcomes but on **your qualities** and **behavior** during a difficult time. _____
_____

229

Volunteer

AGE	DIFFICULTY	PAGES
A & T	2	1

PURPOSE

To do something productive and help others resulting in enhanced esteem.

MATERIALS

Board, marker, magazine pictures of people helping others and/or working and art supplies for the variation. A name and address of a facility to visit, snacks, a regular bingo game and prizes.

ATTENTION GRABBER

Tape pictures on the board and instruct each person to select one. Each sits or stands in front and shares what the person in the picture is gaining from the activity and how it makes the person feel.
Example: An ad showing use of a cleaning product would foster feelings of pride in a person who cleaned the floor; a person helping another would feel needed.
Discuss a project the group can do and work in committees (refreshments, prizes, etc.).

ACTIVITY

After obtaining permission and planning the event, take group to a convalescent hospital or other facility. Pass out snacks. Take turns calling Bingo numbers, helping the players and giving out prizes.

FOLLOW-UP

Debrief afterward – discuss how they felt going to the facility compared with their feeling upon completion. Compare level of anxiety, depression and self-confidence. Discuss periodic return to the same site or related projects they can do as a group or individually. Send group 'thank you note' to the Activity Director who helped facilitate the visit.

VARIATION

I. Before going, make inspirational greeting cards for the patients or residents. Use additional materials (paper, crayons, pencils or pens, and markers) and draw on front and compose own messages or copy inspirational verses. Each participant gives a card to each patient or resident at facility.

II. In December, practice several times then visit a facility and sing Holiday songs. Encourage musically inclined participants to play instruments or direct the choir. Provide colorful carnations for the chorus to wear.

NOTE: To plan the volunteer outing, contact the Activity Director of a skilled nursing home or other facility. Discuss with group in advance their attire, behavior and other expectations.

Encourage expression of concerns or anxiety and elicit concept of facing our fears about challenges and the unknown.

III. Use phone book and publications soliciting volunteers. Each selects an individual site, approaches the Activity Director, plans an activity or visit and shares with group before and after his/her volunteer experience.

NOTE: They may visit ill or elderly patients or offer other services (clerical, mailroom), or "Meals on Wheels" (delivering food to people who are shut-in) and other projects. The planning stage can begin during inpatient treatment. The individual or group visitation can occur during Partial Hospital, Day Treatment or other outpatient programs.

WHAT'S IN A NAME

AGE	DIFFICULTY	PAGES
ALL	2	1

PURPOSE

To identify own and peer attributes by hearing, writing and reading them aloud.

MATERIALS

Board, marker, index cards with each person's name (letters vertical) and an attribute or positive phrase beginning with each letter.

Example: **T** = Thoughtful
O = Optimistic
M = Makes friends easily

ATTENTION GRABBER

Write on board "What's in a Name?"
Volunteer prints name of a famous person on board with letters under each other.
Take turns writing a descriptive word or phrase for each letter on board.

ACTIVITY

Explain "We're going to think of attributes for each peer." Take turns putting own names on board and writing words or phrases suggested by peers. They read each line –
"I am thoughtful. I am optimistic, etc." Have a peer or staff 'recorder' copy the attributes for each name on a separate sheet of paper.

Pass out the index cards (prepared in advance) and have each sit in 'spotlight seat' and read his/her own list of attributes.*
Elicit peer feedback regarding the statements.

FOLLOW-UP

Example: "Who can tell a time Tom made friends easily?" Then each copies his/her own list, developed by peers, on the back of the index card (from the 'recorder's' paper). They keep the index cards and read them daily.

NOTE: * The index card prepared in advance serves as a 'back up' as well as if participants cannot think or a word for a particular letter of someone's name.

OVERVIEW

SELF-HELP is particularly relevant to participants who rely too much on external forces. Misconceptions about luck, misfortune and being rescued immobilize them. Well-meaning people in the helping professions may have contributed to learned-helplessness. Participants become self-reliant by eradicating secondary gains, examining their own roles in setbacks and success, avoiding destructive situations, and meeting their own needs.

LEGEND

AGES:
ALL = ALL ages, 8 or 9 through adults
YP = YOUNG PEOPLE, ages 8 or 9 through 17
T = TEENS, ages 13 through 17
A & T = ADULTS and TEENS, ages 13 and older
A = ADULTS, ages 18 and older
* = SPECIFIC PAGES expressly for this population.

LEVEL OF DIFFICULTY:
1 = EASIER - basic language; minimal reading and writing
2 = MODERATE - introduces new terminology; incorporates life experiences
3 = MORE DIFFICULT - requires some prior knowledge or introduction of new information; promotes peer teaching

PAGES:
The total number of pages related to the activity, including FACILITATOR'S INFORMATION and all accompanying pages.

FACILITATOR'S INFORMATION

DON'T QUIT

AGE	DIFFICULTY	PAGES
A & T	2	2

PURPOSE

To stick to the task despite setbacks.

MATERIALS

Board, marker, 'DON'T QUIT' WORKSHEET, page 236.

ATTENTION GRABBER

Coach volunteer before group to pantomime working with pencil and paper, then crumpling it up and throwing paper in trash. Ask, "What did s/he do?" (gave up on a difficult project). Volunteer writes 'DON'T QUIT' on board. Elicit people's experiences with quitting and/or overcoming obstacles.

ACTIVITY

Distribute worksheet with "You Mustn't Quit" by unknown author and related questions. Read poem in unison a few times and discuss people's interpretations. Allow about fifteen minutes for participants to write answers to worksheet questions. Discuss their responses.

FOLLOW-UP

Each shares at least one insight developed during the activity.

VARIATION

I. Facilitator or volunteers ask worksheet questions while participants answer orally.

II. Divide into dyads. Each asks partner the questions, records responses, then 'presents' partner to the group and encourages feedback. "This is Barbara. She wanted to quit when…"

WORKSHEET

You Mustn't Quit

When things go wrong, as they sometimes will,
When the road you're trudging seems all uphill,
When the funds are low and the debts are high
And you want to smile, but you have to sigh,
When care is pressing you down a bit,
Rest! if you must — but never quit.

Life is queer, with its twists and turns,
As every one of us sometimes learns,
And many a failure turns about
When he might have won if he'd stuck it out;
Stick to your task, though the pace seems slow —
You might succeed with one more blow.

Success is failure turned inside out —
The silver tint of the clouds of doubt —
And you never can tell how close you are,
It may be near when it seems afar;
So stick to the fight when you're hardest hit —
It's when things seem worst that you mustn't quit.

Author Unknown

1. When and how were things going wrong and why did you quit or want to quit working toward a goal? _____ _____ _____ _____

2. When and how did you 'rest' instead of quitting? (Examples: taking a semester off during a crisis or receiving Disability pay until an illness subsides or stabilizes). _____ _____ _____

3. Tell about a time you succeeded 'with one more blow'. _____ _____ _____ _____

4. Explain in your own words: "Success is failure turned inside out". _____ _____ _____

5. When and how did you turn a setback into a steppingstone? _____ _____ _____

6. What is your most difficult current victory that "may be near" but seems "afar"? _____ _____ _____

7. Tell at least three ways you can "stick to the fight". _____ _____ _____

8. According to the last line, when mustn't we quit? _____ _____ _____

FACILITATOR'S INFORMATION
Get Unstuck

AGE	DIFFICULTY	PAGES
A & T	2	1

PURPOSE

To move forward despite adversity.

MATERIALS

Board, marker, masking tape, paper, pencils, crayons.

ATTENTION GRABBER

Volunteer walks into group with circular piece of masking tape stuck to bottom of shoe with sticky side out (to also stick to floor). Show it and ask, "What will happen when s/he tries to walk?" then "What does it mean to be stuck in one spot?" Elicit that past trauma, regrets, future fears, untreated emotional and substance abuse problems can immobilize us.
Write 'Get Unstuck' on board.

ACTIVITY

Each identifies a situation or issue they 'can't get past.'

They write key words on the tape and affix it to their shoes. Example: "Fear, depression, past abuse, no confidence, anger, guilt, hurt, mistrust, laziness, my illness, addiction, ego, false pride", etc.

They draw, write or think about ways to get 'unstuck' and share these with group.
Example: 'Stuck' in the past due to childhood abuse.
To move forward will require individual therapy, support group, reading and doing related workbooks and/or journalizing.

Symbolize getting 'unstuck' by removing tape from shoes and throwing it away.

Be sure to retrieve roll of masking tape after group.

FOLLOW-UP

Brainstorm ways to 'get unstuck' from the PAST:
Examples: Recognize it's over, it cannot be changed. It can't ruin the present unless we let it. We can change our thoughts about it. We are avoiding similar problems today. We can join support groups or work toward related legislation or public awareness regarding the issue.

Brainstorm ways to 'get unstuck' from the FUTURE:
Examples: Many things we worry about never happen. We cannot control other people or circumstances. We can think and/or act in a healthy and safe manner today. We can work towards future well-being through medication, therapy, productive activity, legal action if pertinent, budget our money, nurture positive thoughts and relationships and detach from destructive ones.

LIFELINES

AGE	DIFFICULTY	PAGES
A & T	2	2

PURPOSE Identify our high and low points in life, steps toward achievements and downfalls, realize we all have our 'ups and downs.'

MATERIALS Board, marker, pencils, 'LIFELINES' WORKSHEET, page 239.

ATTENTION GRABBER Ask, "Who has heard of palm reading?", and elicit that some believe palms tell the story of our past and future. Explain we do not promote this belief but we will be looking at our palms today and thinking about our life. Volunteer draws palm on board including a path leading to each finger and the joints to represent rungs of a ladder or milestones.

ACTIVITY Each uses the LIFELINES worksheet and identifies two high points or major achievements (at fingertips) and two low points (between fingers). They label the good decision leading to the high point and two stepping stones or mini-goals (joints) they met before the peak experience. For each 'low point' have them label two pitfalls (downward turns) they passed on the way down.

Example: Peak experience was a career accomplishment. The path (line on palm) was deciding to enter a training course. The 'joints' were completion of course work and landing the entry-level job.

Example: For a person recovering from substance abuse, the path to sobriety is acknowledgment of a problem and the joints may represent taking medicine and going to therapy or attending his/her first meeting and 12-step completion. For the 'downfalls' such as relapse or failing a test, emphasize what led to the 'low point' such as stopping medicine, going to bars, and avoiding meetings or house of worship, watching TV instead of studying.

FOLLOW-UP Each shows and tells about his/her diagram.

LifeLines

Directions: Label at least two of each — high points, low points, good decisions, wrong decisions, stepping stones (toward achievements) and downward turns (toward low points)

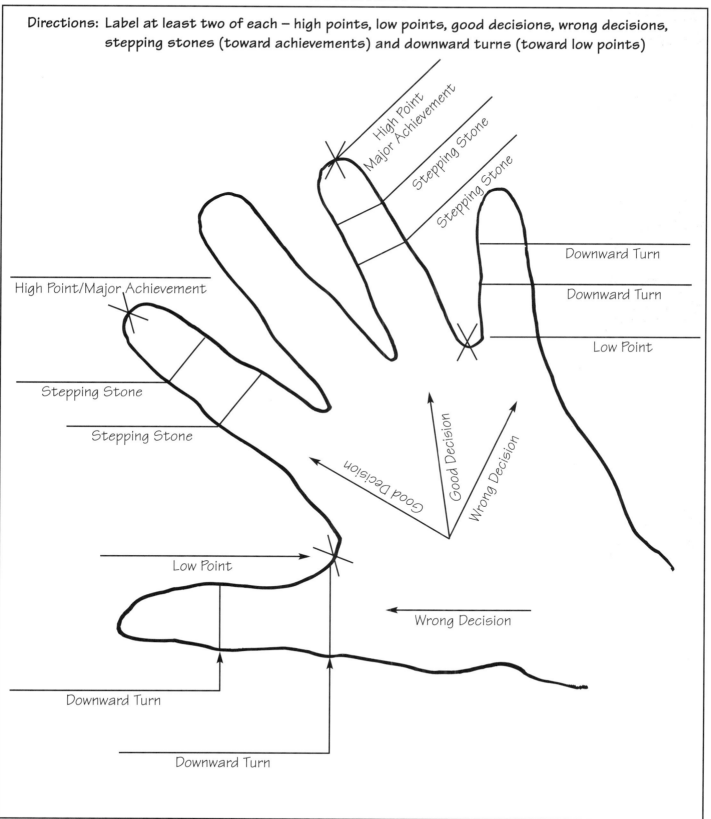

High Point/Major Achievement

High Point/Major Achievement

Stepping Stone

Stepping Stone

Stepping Stone

Stepping Stone

Downward Turn

Downward Turn

Low Point

Good Decision

Good Decision

Wrong Decision

Low Point

Wrong Decision

Downward Turn

Downward Turn

239

FACILITATOR'S INFORMATION
SECONDARY GAINS

AGE	DIFFICULTY	PAGES
ALL	1	3

PURPOSE
Identify reasons we remain dysfunctional or fail to recover and ways to 'get the goodies' positively.

MATERIALS
Board, marker, paper, pencils,
'SECONDARY GAINS' WORKSHEETS, pages 241, 242.

ATTENTION GRABBER
Two volunteers portray a scene. Child tells mom s/he has a stomachache. Mom says, "OK, stay home" and walks out. Child jumps for joy and says "good."
Ask, "What does this child gain from being sick?" Elicit concepts of staying home, avoiding the challenges of school, extra attention from mom, cartoons, etc. Introduce concept of secondary gains.

ACTIVITY
Discuss ways some people get secondary gains. Examples include: Depression, Anger, Addiction, Cutting on Self, Feeling Sick (stomachache, headache). Each person interviews a partner and documents answers on worksheet. Each presents his/her partner's responses to group members who provide feedback. "This is Joe and what he does is . . . "

Example of Handouts, Questions and Answers:
What do you do...? (Act depressed = stay in bed)
What are the short term benefits? (In bed all day = avoid school, work or family responsibilities)
What are the drawbacks? (Do not accomplish anything, low esteem, isolation, no or few friends, conflicts don't get resolved)
What do you need to do? (Get out of bed, be aware of avoidant behavior, engage in activities and face problems)
What are the true gains resulting from the positive behavior? (Productivity, self esteem, companionship, conflict resolution)

FOLLOW-UP
Each shares at least one insight developed through this activity.

VARIATION
On paper or on board, have people complete the columns (addressing their own feelings and behavior)

Negative Behavior	Secondary Gains	Ways to Get True Gains
Examples: Cut on self	Relieve pain and get sympathy	Therapy to help relieve pain
		Get recognition for helping someone or for doing something productive
		Write, draw, clean up a room

240

SECONDARY GAINS

WORKSHEET – SELECT TOPIC: (Possibilities include Depression, Anger, Addiction, Self-Harm, Feeling Sick)

What do you do that is negative and/or harmful?

_____

_____

_____

_____

What short-term benefits do you seem to get? (secondary gains)

_____

_____

_____

_____

What are the drawbacks of the negative behavior?

_____

_____

_____

_____

What can you do to get what you want in a positive and healthy way?

_____

_____

_____

_____

What are your true gains from the positive behavior?

_____

_____

_____

_____

SECONDARY GAINS

WORKSHEET

NEGATIVE BEHAVIOR	SECONDARY GAINS	WAYS TO GET TRUE GAINS

FACILITATOR'S INFORMATION
Self-Help vs. Learned Helplessness

AGE	DIFFICULTY	PAGES
A & T	1	2

PURPOSE

To practice self-determination.

MATERIALS

Board, marker, container for CUT-UPS, 'SELF-HELP' CUT-UPS, page 244.

ATTENTION GRABBER

Volunteer sits on his/her hands while another tries to tickle or pretends to hit him or her. Ask group how the person feels who can't use his/her hands (elicit "helpless").

ACTIVITY

Ask each to share a time s/he felt helpless. Discuss that helplessness and/or hopelessness often stems from past powerlessness.

Print 'Learned Helplessness' on board and discuss.

People take turns reading situations and defining the helpless and helpful responses.

Examples:
1. **You have a toothache.**
   Helpless = Do nothing or ask a parent, nurse or social worker to make you an appointment.
   Self-help = Make own dental appointment.

2. **You have no income.**
   Helpless = Do nothing, beg on the streets or find someone who'll take care of you.
   Self-help = Go to Dept. of Vocational Rehabilitation for job training. Look in help-wanted ads. Apply for public assistance if you are disabled or unable to work.

3. **You have no transportation.**
   Helpless = Go nowhere or hitch rides. Use 'no transportation' as excuse for not working, missing appointments, and not going to school.
   Self-help = Call bus company and ask about bus passes. Save money for a used car. Get a used bicycle. Locate school, work, doctors, and dentist within walking distance.

FOLLOW-UP

Each describes a current situation wherein s/he can take steps toward self-help.

Self-Help vs. Learned Helplessness

1

Someone is physically, sexually or emotionally abusing you.

2

You have a lump in your breast, rectal bleeding or other serious physical symptom.

3

You have very few job skills.

4

You have very little education.

5

You have medicine left for only 3 days and then will run out.

6

You are sick and unable to attend an appointment.

7

Your car broke down and you might miss work.

8

You need glasses.

9

You got a ticket.

10

You cannot afford the rent.

11

You cannot pay your gas, electric or phone bill.

12

You don't know how to do a work or school assignment.

13

You get a poor performance evaluation at work.

14

Your marriage or relationship is failing.

15

You get a 'D' or 'F' on a test.

FACILITATOR'S INFORMATION
THE HOLE

AGE	DIFFICULTY	PAGES
ALL	1	3

PURPOSE

Identify and avoid pitfalls.

MATERIALS

Board, marker and chalk, string or tape,
'AN AUTOBIOGRAPHY IN FIVE SHORT CHAPTERS,' by PORTIA NELSON, page 246,
and 'THE HOLE' WORKSHEET, page 247.
Pencils for VARIATION.

ATTENTION GRABBER

Volunteer draws circle on floor or makes a circle with chalk, string or tape (to represent a hole).
Explain: "That's a hole – we're going to hear a story about it."
(Be sure to retrieve string or tape after group activity).

ACTIVITY

A narrator and actor practice briefly reading and role-playing the autobiography before group time. They now perform for 'audience'.

After the performance, a volunteer asks the questions and participants take turns answering.

FOLLOW-UP

Each identifies which 'chapter' is most relevant to him/her and explains why.

Individuals, dyads or small groups compose poems with messages, then read aloud or role-play for peers.

VARIATION

I. List questions on board or distribute the questions as a worksheet. People write, then share their answers.

II. Divide into dyads. Interview and document partner's responses. 'Present' partner to the group. Example: "This is David and his 'deep hole' is . . . "

THE HOLE

AN AUTOBIOGRAPHY IN FIVE SHORT CHAPTERS
by Portia Nelson

I

I walk down the street
There is a deep hole in the sidewalk.
I fall in
I am lost ….. I am helpless
It isn't my fault.
It takes forever to find a way out.

II

I walk down the same street.
There is a deep hole in the sidewalk.
I pretend I don't see it.
I fall in again.
I can't believe I am in the same place,
but it isn't my fault.
It still takes a long time to get out.

III

I walk down the same street
There is a deep hole in the sidewalk.
I see it is there.
I still fall in….. it's a habit.
My eyes are open. I know where I am.
It is my fault.
I get out immediately.

IV

I walk down the same street
There is a deep hole in the sidewalk.
I walk around it.

V

I walk down another street.

WORKSHEET

1. What is your 'deep hole'? (A problem behavior specific to you.)
   Possible answers are: drinking, drugs, violence, unhealthy relationships, self-harm.
   _____
   _____
   _____
   _____

2. Tell about your chapter #1 — your first fall. Explain how you found a way out.
   _____
   _____
   _____
   _____

3. What is the difference between chapter #1 and #2? What does "I pretend I don't see it" mean and how did you pretend you didn't see your 'hole.'
   _____
   _____
   _____
   _____

4. In chapter #3, why do we fall in? What do we recognize that helps us get out immediately? Tell time you admitted it was your fault and how it helped.
   _____
   _____
   _____
   _____

5. What big difference occurs in chapter #4? Tell a time you 'walked around it.'
   _____
   _____
   _____
   _____

6. What does it mean to 'walk down another street'? Describe your new activities and/or lifestyle. What will you be thinking and doing? What kind of relationships will you seek?
   _____
   _____
   _____
   _____

FACILITATOR'S INFORMATION
TOXIC NOUNS

	AGE	DIFFICULTY	PAGES
	ALL	1	2

PURPOSE
Identify people, places and things to avoid and beneficial replacements or substitutes.

MATERIALS
Board, marker, clipboards, pencils, 'TOXIC NOUNS' WORKSHEET, page 249.

ATTENTION GRABBER
Ask participants to recall Science and English classes and write 'toxic' on board. Ask for definition. Write 'noun' and ask what it means. Elicit concept that dangerous or unhealthy people, places and things are avoidable and replaceable.

ACTIVITY
Use worksheets or list three columns on board. In dyads, small groups, teams or as a whole group, brainstorm the people, places and things to avoid, and their positive replacements or substitutes.

FOLLOW-UP
Ask, "What are 'toxic thoughts' ?" (negative)
Each gives an example of a current toxic thought and a positive but realistic substitution.

VARIATION
Have some group members work only on people, others on places and others on things to avoid. Then list these on board and discuss why each is 'toxic' and identify replacements.

Example:

PEOPLE	PLACES	THINGS
Drinkers	Bars	Beer in refrigerator
Gang Bangers	Gang Neighborhoods	Weapons
SUBSTITUTES	**SUBSTITUTES**	**SUBSTITUTES**
Sober friends	Meetings	12-step books
Teammates	Gym and/or playing fields	Tennis shoes and/or sports equipment

WORKSHEET

PEOPLE	PLACES	THINGS

SUBSTITUTES	SUBSTITUTES	SUBSTITUTES

FACILITATOR'S INFORMATION
Victim vs. Victor

AGE	DIFFICULTY	PAGES
ALL	1	2

PURPOSE

Practice identifying survivor strength.

MATERIALS

Board, marker, blanket, cup of water, paper, pencils or crayons, 'VICTIM vs VICTOR' WORKSHEET, page 251.

ATTENTION GRABBER

Volunteer writes 'VICTIM vs VICTOR' on board.
One person pretends to push another off a chair. The victim states "My leg is broken".
Another peer tells him/her to lie down, brings a blanket and water to comfort him/her.
Ask: "What was going on in the role play? What does it mean to be a victim?
    Are there any benefits?"
Elicit concept of secondary gains.
Example: You get attention and sympathy.
    (People take care of you. You're not expected to go to work or school.)

ACTIVITY

Have each share a time s/he was a victim and a time s/he rose above adversity.
Discuss importance of recognizing victimizing situations and self-pity and how to get help from others, ourselves and our Higher Power. Advise people to consider emotional victimization (not just physical illness or injury as in the Attention Grabber).

Distribute worksheets. People draw or sketch a current situation wherein they feel like a victim, then draw or sketch themselves victorious.

Example: Victim lying in bed with negative thoughts depicted in cartoon fashion such as "The past has ruined me." On the VICTOR side, they draw themselves out of bed, at therapy, at support groups, doing schoolwork, praying (if applicable), doing enjoyable hobbies or activities, volunteering, etc.

FOLLOW-UP

They share their victim and victor pictures and receive feedback from peers.

VICTIM vs. VICTOR

VICTIM	VICTOR

SELF-REFLECTION

SELF-REFLECTION requires introspection. Bingo elicits disclosure, feedback and insight regarding relationships, medication, mental health and substance abuse recovery.

ACTIVITY	PAGE NUMBERS	AGE	LEVEL OF DIFFICULTY	PAGES
BINGO	255	—	—	1
Coping	256	A & T	2	1
Coping – Teens	257	*T	1	1
Favorites	258	*YP	1	1
Insight I	259	ALL	1	1
Insight II	260	A & T	2	1
Medicine	261	ALL	2	1
Relationships	262	A & T	1	1
Substance Abuse Recovery I	263	ALL	2	1
Substance Abuse Recovery II	264	ALL	2	1
Substance Abuse Recovery III	265	A & T	2	1

LEGEND

AGES:
ALL = ALL ages, 8 or 9 through adults
YP = YOUNG PEOPLE, ages 8 or 9 through 17
T = TEENS, ages 13 through 17
A & T = ADULTS and TEENS, ages 13 and older
A = ADULTS, ages 18 and older
* = SPECIFIC PAGES expressly for this population.

LEVEL OF DIFFICULTY:
1 = EASIER - basic language; minimal reading and writing
2 = MODERATE - introduces new terminology; incorporates life experiences
3 = MORE DIFFICULT - requires some prior knowledge or introduction of new information; promotes peer teaching

PAGES: The total number of pages related to the activity, including FACILITATOR'S INFORMATION and all accompanying pages.

BINGO

PG	ACTIVITY	AGE	DIFFICULTY	PAGES
256	Coping	A & T	2	1
257	Coping – Teens	*T	1	1
258	Favorites	*YP	1	1
259	Insight I	ALL	1	1
260	Insight II	A & T	2	1
261	Medicine	ALL	2	1
262	Relationships	A & T	1	1
263	Substance Abuse Recovery I	ALL	2	1
264	Substance Abuse Recovery II	ALL	2	1
265	Substance Abuse Recovery III	A & T	2	1

PURPOSE

Promote introspection, disclosure and helpful concepts.

MATERIALS

'BINGO' cards, pages 256-265, markers, prizes or play money (SKILLS BILLS, pages 277, 278).
Make copies of cards on copy machine.
Use brightly colored paper, if available.
Number the squares on each card differently.
Markers can be pencils or crayons (color the squares or mark 'x') or small objects such as candy to place on the squares.

ATTENTION GRABBER

Ask – "Who has played BINGO? Tell us how it's played." Explain: "With this BINGO, letters and numbers are called. If you have the square, you must answer the question before you place your marker. People win if they get a horizontal, vertical or diagonal row or four corners. If someone does not know an answer, s/he asks the group for help. There are no right or wrong answers except no glamorizing suicide, homicide, violence or substance abuse." Encourage genuine disclosure versus superficiality but do not probe (causes discomfort and slows the pace). Let people respond within their comfort zones.

ACTIVITY

Call letters and numbers. They take turns answering and the first winner has first choice of prize or gets largest denomination of SKILLS BILLS. People do not clear their boards; instead all continue to play. The first winner may continue with his/her card or may become the 'caller' of letters and numbers until the next winner who chooses to take turn at calling. (See 'BINGO' cards, pages 256-265.) Each player can have card relevant to his/her age and/or issues or all may have the same topic.

FOLLOW-UP

Each tells a new insight developed during group.

VARIATION

Distribute sheets 20-30 minutes before game.
Participants write answers, then read responses during BINGO.

COPING

B 1-10	**I** 11-20	**N** 21-30	**G** 31-40	**O** 41-50
Give an example of negative self-talk.	What is 'All or Nothing' thinking?	What are my physical needs?	I act too independent when I _____ _____.	Give an example of a negative thought, feeling and action.
Give an example of positive self-talk.	One behavior I need to change is_____ _____.	What are my safety and security needs?	I am too dependent on _____ for _____.	Give an example of a positive thought, feeling, and action.
When did I jump to conclusions?	I give myself credit for _____ _____.	**FREE**	How do I clear the air with someone?	I minimized a problem when _____ _____.
What is constructive criticism?	A compliment to myself is _____.	How do I meet my love and belonging needs?	What are two ground rules for fair fighting?	I magnified a problem when _____ _____.
What is destructive criticism?	Compliment someone else in the room.	Rate my self-esteem (0-10). How can I raise it?	Why is it important to listen to the other person's side?	Name one feeling underlying my anger.

COPING - TEENS

B 1-10	**I** 11-20	**N** 21-30	**G** 31-40	**O** 41-50
I came to the program because _____ .	A poor way to handle fear is _____ .	What are mood swings?	My family and I argue most about _____ _____ .	My favorite sport to play is _____ .
A poor way to handle anger is _____ .	A good way to handle fear is _____ .	What is denial?	What I like best about school/work is _____ _____ .	My favorite sport to watch is _____ .
A helpful way to handle anger is _____ .	Something positive about myself is _____ .	**FREE**	What I dislike most about school or work is _____ .	My favorite food is _____ .
A poor way to handle depression is _____ .	A benefit of medicine is _____ .	Alcohol causes _____ .	My favorite musical group or star is _____ .	My biggest problem is _____ .
A good way to handle depression is _____ .	A side effect of medicine is _____ .	Street drugs cause _____ .	My favorite TV show is _____ .	My best coping skill is _____ .

257

FAVORITES

B 1-10	**I** 11-20	**N** 21-30	**G** 31-40	**O** 41-50
My favorite color is _____.	My favorite TV show is _____.	What I like best about myself is: _____.	The most important thing I have learned is: _____.	A helpful way to handle fear is _____.
My favorite animal is _____.	My favorite sport is _____.	My favorite subject in school is or was: _____.	The job I (would) like to do is _____.	Talking helps because _____.
My favorite food is _____.	My favorite day of the week is _____.	**FREE**	What makes me laugh is _____.	Time alone helps because _____.
My favorite song is _____.	My favorite month is _____.	What I like best about this program is _____.	A helpful way to handle anger is _____.	I believe in _____.
My favorite holiday is _____.	One of my favorite people is _____.	My favorite clothes are _____.	A helpful way to handle sadness is _____.	Medicine helps me by _____.

258

INSIGHT I

B 1-10	**I** 11-20	**N** 21-30	**G** 31-40	**O** 41-50
Explain: Things do not change. We change.	I have learned: _____ _____.	I will "act as if" _____ _____ when _____.	The past won't ruin my present or future if _____ _____.	Two ways I get energy are: _____ _____.
What is GREAT in my life right now?	The only one who can save me is _____ because _____ _____.	I can be more loving toward _____ by _____.	I am necessary because _____ _____.	Two ways I get confidence are _____ _____.
Two GREAT things about me now are _____ _____.	My Higher Power/ Being or Creator is helping me to:	**FREE**	I was assertive when I _____ _____.	To get good friends, I must _____ _____.
Something I cannot change is _____ _____.	A fear I no longer have is _____ _____.	My happiness depends on _____ _____.	I handle anger positively when _____ _____.	To be loved, I must _____ _____.
Something I CAN change NOW is _____ _____.	My success begins with my _____ _____.	I have decided _____ _____.	When someone else is angry, I _____ _____.	I can teach others _____ _____.

INSIGHT II

B 1-10	**I** 11-20	**N** 21-30	**G** 31-40	**O** 41-50
How have I tried to change my life by manipulating my environment?	Who do I need to set firmer boundaries with?	I lacked humility when _____ _____.	When I 'mind read' I usually think _____ _____.	What is a healthy risk I should take?
In what area do I want to do well but continue to sabotage myself?	What am I in a 'rat race' about?	I catastrophize about _____ _____.	When I 'fortune tell', I usually think _____ _____.	I feel best about myself when I _____ _____.
An example of my self-will is _____ _____.	I will love myself regardless of _____ _____.	**FREE**	A time I took something personally was _____ _____.	I have made these changes recently _____ _____.
I need to surround myself with people who _____ _____.	What is unconditional self-love for me?	I magnify this problem _____ _____.	I depend too much on _____ _____ for my happiness.	My body is thankful to me when _____ _____.
What is driving me to negative behaviors (drink, use or hurt myself)?	I was humble when _____ _____.	I minimize this problem: _____ _____.	I know I'm going downhill when _____ _____.	I am inspired by: _____ _____.

260

MEDICINE

B 1-10	I 11-20	N 21-30	G 31-40	O 41-50
What symptoms are treated by antidepressants?	What is a benefit of taking medicine?	Give the name of a medicine you are on and the reason.	What helps if a medicine upsets your stomach?	Name 3 reasons people refuse medicines and provide rebuttals.
Dosage means _____.	What is a side effect?	What symptoms are treated by antipsychotics?	When should you stop taking your medicine?	If you get a rash, what should you do?
Frequency means _____.	What is a chemical imbalance?	FREE	If you have muscle stiffness or you shake, what should you do?	What is a mood stabilizer?
Why is blood drawn when you are on some medicines?	What is an antianxiety medicine?	What helps with constipation?	What can you do if you get a headache from your medicine?	How long does it usually take for most medicines to be fully effective?
What helps with dry mouth?	What helps with sedation?	What helps if you get dizzy when you get up quickly?	Why are liver and/or kidney function tests done with some medicines?	What happens if you drink alcohol or use street drugs with your medicine?

RELATIONSHIPS

B 1-10	**I** 11-20	**N** 21-30	**G** 31-40	**O** 41-50
3 things about my first love are: _____ _____ _____ .	One thing I need in a relationship is _____ _____ _____ .	A relationship that brings me joy is _____ _____ _____ .	Safe sex means _____ _____	My best past relationship was with _____ _____ .
My favorite romantic song is _____ _____ .	I will not tolerate _____ _____ in a relationship.	Who can I trust?	How important is my family's approval of my partner?	My best relationship now is with _____ _____ .
How could romance be dangerous to recovery?	Define the difference between love and lust.	**FREE**	How can I handle a break-up?	Is it better to have loved and lost than to never have loved? Why?
I meet my need for love and belonging by _____ _____ .	Two steps in conflict resolution are _____ _____ .	A dangerous place to meet people is _____ _____ .	How does or could medicines affect my love life?	Tolerance means _____ _____ .
Do opposites attract? Why or why not?	What good can come from arguing?	A fairly safe place to meet people is _____ _____ .	Two ways to show my love are: _____ _____ .	Forgiving is necessary because _____ _____ .

262

SUBSTANCE ABUSE RECOVERY I

B 1-10	I 11-20	N 21-30	G 31-40	O 41-50
How is a family like a mobile?	What is healthy selfishness?	I got angry when _____ complained about my drinking and/or using.	My slippery situation is _____.	The difference between a slip and a relapse is _____.
Who has enabled me and how?	Who and/or what do I blame for my drinking or using?	AA or NA helps me by _____.	How can I redirect my activity?	What could lead to relapse for me?
What is 'white knuckling?'	My addictive self is _____.	FREE	I felt guilty about my drinking or drug use when _____.	How can I reach out for help?
What am I too passive about?	My sober self is _____.	I self medicated when _____.	I used an 'eye opener' when _____.	How can I change my thinking?
What do I need to be assertive about?	I tried to cut down when _____.	I am in denial about _____.	How do I resolve conflicts?	How can I change my emotions?

SUBSTANCE ABUSE RECOVERY II

B 1-10	**I** 11-20	**N** 21-30	**G** 31-40	**O** 41-50
I was in denial when _____.	I feel abandoned when _____.	I am assertive when I _____.	I am grateful for _____.	My 'telephone therapist' is _____.
A character strength of time is _____.	I tried to rationalize when _____.	I need to be assertive when _____.	"Easy does it" for me means _____.	An old idea of mine about alcohol or drugs is _____.
Sponsors and step work help by _____.	Explain benefits of 'sharing our stuff.'	**FREE**	I would like to change _____ about myself.	I now know this about alcohol and/or drugs:
I feel angry when _____.	A weakness of mine is _____.	My idea of a healthy relationship is _____.	What does "First things first" mean to me?	When I feel sorry for myself, I _____.
I feel hurt when _____.	I am a caring person when _____.	I can be good to myself by _____.	If I think about drinking or using, I need to _____.	I can overcome loneliness by _____.

SUBSTANCE ABUSE RECOVERY III

B I N G O

B 1-10	I 11-20	N 21-30	G 31-40	O 41-50
How has using drugs and/or alcohol affected my body?	What is 'craving'?	Chronic disease means _____ _____.	What is AA or NA?	A time I was paranoid from or about my use was _____.
Name two emotional effects of substance abuse.	Explain physical tolerance.	Progressive means _____ _____.	What is substitution?	Two dangerous things I did under the influence were _____ and _____.
Name two legal consequences.	My life is unmanageable because _____ _____.	FREE	What is a relapse?	How can substance abuse affect my sex life?
How has substance abuse affected my relationships?	Name two possible causes of substance abuse.	I can stay sober "one day at a time" by _____ _____.	How can we prevent relapse?	Describe my Higher Power:
How has it affected my finances?	I knew I was powerless over substance abuse when _____.	A myth about substance abuse is _____.	A time I got sick from it was _____.	I knew I was sick and tired when _____.

STRESS MANAGEMENT

STRESS MANAGEMENT is essential to avoid exacerbation of emotional and addiction symptoms. Mental illness, thought distortions, defense mechanisms, self harm, violence and alcohol or drug cravings worsen during stress. Participants see that serenity comes from within, despite chaotic conditions. They practice relaxation techniques, act within their power to rectify stressful situations and learn to ' let go'. Coming out of their 'comfort zones' to gradually experience positive stress is expedited.

ACTIVITY	PAGE NUMBERS	AGE	LEVEL OF DIFFICULTY	PAGES
Calm In Chaos	269 - 270	ALL	1	2
Comfort Zones	271 - 272	ALL	1	2
Past, Present and Future	273 - 274	ALL	1	2
Practice Makes Better	275 - 276	ALL	1	2

CALM IN CHAOS

AGE	DIFFICULTY	PAGES
ALL	1	2

PURPOSE

Develop internal locus of control.

MATERIALS

Board, marker, 'CALM IN CHAOS' WORKSHEET, page 270.

ATTENTION GRABBER

Volunteer divides the board in half with vertical line and labels one side CALM, and the other side CHAOS.

ACTIVITY

Discuss the terms. Group members take turns drawing and adding components of a peaceful scene as in a collage on CALM side. (Lake, trees, clouds or mountains or they may add a book or music or whatever signifies peacefulness.) Do the same for CHAOS. Each adds anxiety inducing things (a test, job interview, public speaking, dark clouds, rain, etc.) Each places his/her initials on the side where s/he feels the most peace (most or all will choose the CALM side).

Ask anyone who chose CHAOS how s/he remains calm amidst chaos.

Ask "Is it possible to be anxious in the calm situation?" (We can be very anxious in a peaceful environment – example would be sitting in our own bedroom an hour before an important test or a first date.)

Each tells a time his/her environment was calm but s/he was nervous.

Ask, "How we can be calm amidst chaos?" Each tells a time s/he maintained composure amidst turmoil. For people never calm in chaos, ask, "Think or a stressful situation – How did you survive?"Discuss cognitive and behavioral ways to remain calm in chaos.
    Example:
    Thoughts – "I'll survive" and "This will pass."
    Actions – deep breathing and visualizing ourselves overcoming the situation; prayer,
        affirmations or meditation.

FOLLOW-UP

Distribute worksheet.

Each draws current or potential stressors in the CHAOS column and depicts how s/he will handle them in the CALM column. Participants share their work and receive feedback.

CALM IN CHAOS

WORKSHEET

CHAOS Draw your stressors.	CALM Draw how you'll handle your stressors.

COMFORT ZONES

AGE	DIFFICULTY	PAGES
ALL	1	2

PURPOSE

To recognize change is stressful but beneficial; to identify positive stress; to gradually de-sensitize by taking 'baby steps' outside 'comfort zones'.

MATERIALS

Board, marker, pencils and crayons, 'COMFORT ZONES' WORKSHEET, page 272. (Optional) if participants usually sit in the same chairs, before group place name labels on different seats and instruct them to sit accordingly.

ATTENTION GRABBER

If participants are sitting in different seats, ask, "How did you feel when told to sit according to your name labels?" Most will express mild discomfort. Elicit that even small changes can cause stress. Volunteer, coached before group, draws caterpillar in cocoon on board (offer graphics on page __ for a cue) and asks peers, "What's this?" S/he then asks a volunteer to draw the next phase of development. Volunteer depicts butterfly. Explain that we, like caterpillars, undergo metamorphosis or transformation.

ACTIVITY

Ask, "Would most people rather be a butterfly or caterpillar? Why?" (most will choose butterfly because of its beauty and flying ability) Ask, "Why would some people choose to remain a caterpillar?" (cocoon is comfortable and safe) Ask "How are we like caterpillars ?" Elicit concepts: We change and become more capable; change can be positive but stressful.

Volunteer writes COCOONS = COMFORT ZONES and lists on board while peers brainstorm examples which may include isolating in bed, room, or home; being around people physically but avoiding conversation; wrapping 'illness' around us like a cocoon to avoid school, volunteering, hobbies, community activities, social events, responsibilities or relationships; using alcohol or drugs to create a false sense of ease or euphoria. Volunteer lists as peers brainstorm advantages and disadvantages of cocoons and comfort zones. Advantages include comfort and safety; disadvantages include confinement and stagnation.

Volunteer writes CHANGES = STRESS ZONES and lists examples which may include getting out of bed, room or house; talking to people; starting school, work, volunteer job, hobbies, community activities, relationships; joining a support group; assuming responsibilities; facing life clean and sober. Volunteer lists as peers brainstorm advantages and disadvantages of change. Advantages include excitement, accomplishment, friendship, recognition, and esteem; disadvantages include temporary nervousness, fear of failure, fear of success and accompanying performance pressures.

Discuss concept of 'baby steps' toward change. Examples: talking to one unfamiliar person each day; making one phone call today and two tomorrow about school or volunteer work; getting a library book about a prospective hobby, then visiting a shop to ask questions about supplies; getting a schedule of support groups, then attending one with a 'buddy'.

FOLLOW-UP

Distribute 'COMFORT ZONES' WORKSHEET, page 272. Allow about fifteen minutes to complete, then take turns in 'spotlight seat', sharing answers and receiving peer feedback.

VARIATION

I. Facilitator or volunteer reads worksheet questions while participants answer orally.

II. Divide into dyads. Each asks partner the worksheet questions, records responses, then 'presents' partner to group. "This is Mike. His cocoon was…"

COMFORT ZONES

1. What is your 'cocoon'? _____
_____

2. At least two advantages of your cocoon are_____
_____

3. At least three disadvantages of your cocoon are_____
_____

4. What is the most important and stressful change you would like to make? _____
_____

5. What are you afraid might happen if you make the change?_____
_____

6. How could you handle the 'worst case scenario'? Examples include accepting a rejection and seeking another relationship; failing one class and taking it over or deciding on a different course of study. _____
_____

7. What rewards might result from the change?_____
_____

8. Create a cartoon or series of drawings. You may use stick figures and symbols. Use the back of this page if necessary. Depict these scenes: you in your 'cocoon' or 'comfort zone'; you breaking out; you taking at least three 'baby steps" toward the change; you handling the challenges and rewards of becoming a 'butterfly'.

FACILITATOR'S INFORMATION
Past, Present
and Future

AGE	DIFFICULTY	PAGES
ALL	1	2

PURPOSE

To categorize concerns as past, present and future;
to differentiate what can and cannot be done; to productively handle stressors.

MATERIALS

Board, marker, calendar, 'PAST, PRESENT AND FUTURE' WORKSHEET, page 244.
Pencils and paper for VARIATION.

ATTENTION GRABBER

Volunteer holds up calendar and asks, "What do calendars show?" Another volunteer divides board into three vertical columns and labels them PAST, PRESENT AND FUTURE. Explain "Worries fall into these categories. 'Past' means yesterday and before, 'future' means tomorrow and after, and ' present' means today."

ACTIVITY

Participants brainstorm as volunteer lists problems in PAST column. Examples: prior abuse, guilt, arrests, financial losses, broken relationships, death of loved ones, poor grades or job performance.

Another volunteer lists as peers brainstorm FUTURE items. Examples: bills, potential illness or injury (self and loved ones), fears of school or work failure, anticipated family feuds or relationship break-ups, possible relapse (worsened symptoms of mental illness and/or substance abuse).

Another volunteer lists under PRESENT **only** immediate concerns. Examples: homelessness, current abuse, ongoing conflicts, today's school or work demands. Ask, "Which list is shortest?" (PRESENT) "Why?" (Most stress relates to the past or future).

Ask, "Can we change the past?" (no) "Can we control the future?" (no) "What **can** we control?" (**today's** thoughts and actions).

Participants take turns going to board, selecting a <u>PRESENT</u> stressor and discussing what **can** be done **today**. Examples: calling shelters for homeless people or victims of abuse; asking teacher or boss how we can improve; reviewing and role-playing conflict resolution techniques; and making appointment for family or relationship counseling.

Take turns selecting <u>PAST</u> worries and discussing what **can** be done **today**. Examples: participate in therapy addressing abuse, guilt, grief and loss; decide that resentment hurts us more than the person we resent; decide to forgive self and others; find out **whether** and **how** we can repair financial, legal, school, work or relationship problems; plan ways to avoid repeating mistakes. **After doing what can be done today, let it go!**

Take turns selecting <u>FUTURE</u> concerns and discussing what **can** be done **today**. Examples: develop a budget; make calls about financial aid, employment, credit counseling, utility assistance, food stamps; make doctor appointments; do preventive maintenance on vehicles, home and equipment; develop a study schedule; request tutoring; ask for a work performance review and develop a plan for improving or advancing; develop a relapse prevention plan encompassing medication, therapy, support groups, written assignments, exercise, nutrition, rest, appropriate socialization and other components. **After doing what can be done today, let it go!**

FOLLOW-UP

Write this quote on board: "Having done all stand."
Discuss its relevance.
Each shares his/her major stressor and receives feedback about 'all' s/he can do today.

VARIATION

People write stressors on slips of paper anonymously. Collect in container. Take turns writing them on board under PAST, PRESENT or FUTURE and discuss what **can** be done **today**.

PAST. PRESENT AND FUTURE

WORKSHEET

PAST STRESSORS	PRESENT STRESSORS	FUTURE STRESSORS
1 . I was mean to someone.	1 . No food.	1 . Worry I'll get cancer.
2 .	2 .	2 . Afraid I'll fail a test.
3 .	3 .	3 .
4 .	4 .	4 .
5 .	5 .	5 .
6 .	6 .	6 .
7 .	7 .	7 .
8 .	8 .	8 .

Things I <u>can</u> do TODAY about the past.	Things I <u>can</u> do TODAY about the present.	Things I <u>can</u> do TODAY about the future.
1 . Apologize and make appointment for Anger Management Class.	1 . Call Food Stamp Agency, Emergency Food Kitchen, and/or Shelters and tell social worker.	1 . Make doctor appointment.
2 .	2 .	2 . Make study schedule and stick to it.
3 .	3 .	3 .
4 .	4 .	4 .
5 .	5 .	5 .
6 .	6 .	6 .
7 .	7 .	7 .
8 .	8 .	8 .
I did what I can do today – Now I will Let It Go!	*I did what I can do today – Now I will Let It Go!*	*I did what I can do today – Now I will Let It Go!*

PRACTICE MAKES BETTER

AGE	DIFFICULTY	PAGES
ALL	1	2

PURPOSE

Demonstrate and practice relaxation.

MATERIALS

Board, marker, RELAXATION TECHNIQUES 'BLURBS' CUT-UPS, page 276, wherein techniques are briefly explained (deep breathing, counting backwards from 100, progressive muscle relaxation, visualization, and others).

ATTENTION GRABBER

Before group, coach volunteer on deep breathing.
S/he walks in, sits down, and without a word, breathes deeply several times.
Ask, "What is s/he doing?" and "Why?"
Write 'RELAXATION TECHNIQUES' on board and explain,
    "We'll be practicing and teaching each other."

ACTIVITY

Each chooses a 'BLURB', reads and practices for 5 minutes, then takes a turn explaining,
    demonstrating and coaching as peers practice.
Seven 'BLURBS' are provided. If there are more than seven participants, they may work in dyads
    or small groups, or participants or leader may develop additional 'BLURBS'.

FOLLOW-UP

Each tells his/her favorite. People share their own techniques not already addressed.

VARIATION

Develop anger management or mood elevation blurbs for this peer teaching activity.

PRACTICE MAKES BETTER

RELAXATION TECHNIQUES 'BLURBS'

Deep breathe — in through your nose slowly and out through mouth 10 times.

Progressive Muscle Relaxation — start with your feet and go up to your head — contract then relax muscles 5 times (feet, legs, abdomen, buttocks, arms, hands, face).

Visualize a time and/or place when you felt totally relaxed. Tell about the sights, sounds, smells, and physical sensations you experienced. Close eyes and recapture it.

Recall or compose a comforting sentence or phrase and repeat it 10 times.
(Example: "I can do this." or "This too shall pass.")

Run in place for two minutes or do 20 jumping jacks.

Set aside 10 minutes to worry about everything. Write list of worries and add to them as troubling thoughts arise. Place in the freezer when done and do not think about the issues for 24 hours (until tomorrow's worry time).

Count backwards from 100.

$KILL$ BILL$

$10 $10

$10 $10

$10 $10

$10 $10

$10 $10

$10 $10

$5 $5

$5 $5

$5 $5

$5 $5

$5 $5

$5 $5

277

$KILL$ BILL$

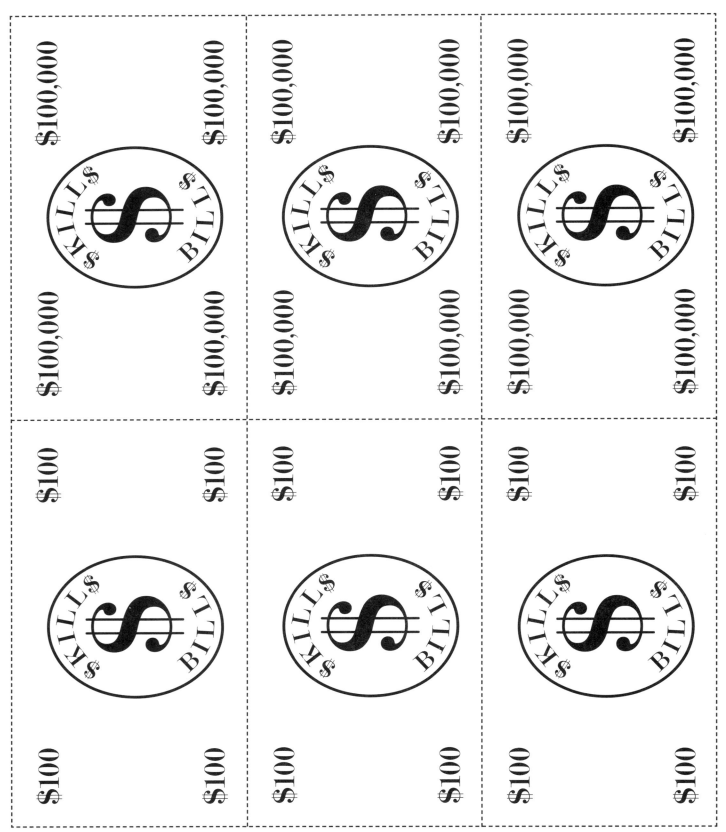

278

REFERENCES

Alexander, A.L., <u>Poems That Touch the Heart</u>, Doubleday, New York, 1956.

Burns, D.D., <u>Ten Days to Self-Esteem</u>, William Morrow and Co., Inc., New York, 1993.

Houseman, C., <u>Psychiatric Certification Review Guide</u>, Health Leadership Associates, Maryland 1994.

Isaacs, A., <u>Mental Health and Psychiatric Nursing</u>, Lippincott-Raven Publishers, Philadelphia, PA., 1996.

Lego, S., <u>Psychiatric Nursing: A Compehensive Reference</u> 2nd ed., Lippincott-Raven Publishers, Philadelphia, PA., 1996.

Mathewson, K.M., <u>Pharmacotherapeutics: A Nursing Process Approach</u>, F.A. Davis Co., Philadelphia, PA., 1991.

Pervin, L.A. and O.P. Jordan, <u>Personality Theory and Research</u> 7th ed., John Wiley and Sons, New York, 1997.

Rinder, E.C., "Combined Group Process-Psychoeducation Model for Psychiatric Clients and Their Families," <u>Journal of Psychosocial Nursing and Mental Health Services</u>, Vol. 38, No. 9, Sept. 2000, pp.34-41.

Rollant, P.D., and D.B. Deppoliti, <u>Mental Health Nursing</u>, Mosby Yearbook, Inc., St. Louis, MO., 1996.

Salzman, C., <u>Psychiatric Medications for Older Adults-The Concise Guide</u>, The Guilford Press, New York, 2001.

Skidmore-Roth, L., <u>Nursing Drug Reference</u>, Mosby, Inc., St. Louis, MO., 1999.

ACKNOWLEDGEMENTS - POETRY and QUOTATIONS

I express gratitude to the authors, publishers and copyright owners whose literature greatly enriches this book.

Alcoholics Anonymous excerpts, reprinted with permission of Alcoholics Anonymous World Services, Inc., New York, NY.

An Autobiography in Five Short Chapters, copyright 1993 by Portia Nelson from the book *There's A Hole In My Sidewalk*, Beyond Words Publishing, Hillsboro, Oregon USA.

Desiderata, copyright 1927 by Max Ehrmann. All rights reserved. Reprinted by permission of Robert L. Bell, Melrose, Mass.

If, by Rudyard Kipling, reprinted by permission of A.P.Watt Ltd. On behalf of The National Trust for places of Historical Interest or Natural Beauty, London.

Outwitted, by Edwin Markham, reprinted by permission of Horrmann Library, Wagner College, Staten Island, New York.

The Road Not Taken, from *The Poetry of Robert Frost* edited by Edward Connery Latham, copyright 1969 by Henry Holt & Co., LLC. Reprinted by permission of Henry Holt & Co., LLC, New York, NY.

Shoot For The Moon excerpts, by Meiji Stewart, copyright 1996 by Meiji Stewart. Reprinted by permission of Hazelden Foundation, Center City, MN.

Wellness Reproductions Makes It Easy To Order!

ORDER ONLINE 24-HOURS A DAY, CALL, FAX or MAIL US

① BILLING INFORMATION

First Name   Last Name   MI

Title or Initials   Department

Organization/Facility

Street Address   Suite or Apt. No.

City   State   Zip + four

Phone   Fax

E-mail Address

SHIPPING INFORMATION *(IF another address or your business address):*

First Name   Last Name   MI

Title or Initials   Department

Organization/Facility

Street Address   Suite or Apt. No.

City   State   Zip + four

Phone   Fax

E-mail Address

② ORDERING INFORMATION

Order Code	Name of Product/Description	Page No.	Quantity	Price Each	Total Price
PRDW71652	100 Interactive Activities — for Mental Health and Substance Abuse Recovery	—		$ 54.95	

③ PAYMENT METHOD

☐ Check or money order in U.S. funds.
☐ Purchase Order (must be attached) P.O. # _____

☐ Visa   VISA   ☐ MasterCard MasterCard   ☐ American Express AMERICAN EXPRESS

Account Number   Expiration Date

Print Name _____   Signature (required) _____

Subtotal	
*Shipping & Handling	
Subtotal	
NY and OH Sales Tax	
GRAND TOTAL	

100% **GUARANTEE:** *Wellness Reproductions & Publishing, LLC stands behind its products 100%.* We will refund, exchange or credit your account for the price of any materials returned **within 30 days** of receipt (excluding shipping). ALL MERCHANDISE NEEDS TO BE IN PERFECT, RESALE-ABLE CONDITION. Simply call us at 1-800-669-9208 for a return authorization number.

IMPORTANT INFORMATION: Our Order Policies ensure fast, efficient service!

Ordering Made Easy!
Have your order code ready!

Online
www.wellness-resources.com
(with credit card – **secured!**)

Call **1.800.669.9208**

Fax **1.800.501.8120**
Toll-Free 24-hours/7 days

Mail
**Wellness Reproductions
& Publishing, LLC**
135 Dupont St.• P.O. Box 760
Plainview, NY 11803-0760

*SHIPPING & HANDLING:
REGULAR GROUND: Add *10% (minimum $5.95)* in 48 contiguous states.
For Alaska, Hawaii, Puerto Rico, Canada and all other international locations; and for rush, express or overnight delivery, please call for rates and delivery information.
Shipments outside of the United States may be subject to additional handling charges and fees. Customers are responsible for any applicable taxes and duties.

PAYMENT METHOD:
CHECK: Make your check payable to *Wellness Reproductions & Publishing, LLC.*
OPEN ACCOUNT: We accept purchase orders from recognized public or private institutions. New accounts please call for information on how to set up an account.
P.O. TERMS: Purchase orders, net 30 days.

CREDIT CARDS: Please include account number, expiration date and your signature.
F.O.B. NY. All international orders must be prepaid in U.S. Funds.

OTHER:
SALES TAX: New York and Ohio residents, add sales tax on total, including shipping and handling. Tax-exempt organizations, please provide exempt or resale number when ordering.

DELIVERY: We ship all in-stock items within the contiguous 48 states via UPS or USPS. Back orders are items that are currently out of stock, but will be shipped to you as soon as possible. There is no additional cost for shipping and handling of back orders if shipped separately from your original order. Please allow up to 7-10 working days for delivery.

PRICING: This order form supersedes all previous order forms. Prices subject to change without notice. If this form has expired, we will bill you any difference in price.

UNIVERSITY INSTRUCTOR? If you are considering using this book as a school text or supplemental resource, please call our office to discuss desk copies and quantity education discounts.

UPDATE OUR MAILING LIST: You are automatically added to our mailing list when you order your first product from us. If you want to change your address, remove your name, or eliminate duplicate names from our file, please contact us. We sometimes make available our mailing list to outside parties. If you do not wish to have your information shared, please let us know.